W9-CFD-511

How To Read
Schematic Diagrams

by
Donald E. Herrington

Howard W. Sams & Co., Inc.
4300 WEST 62ND ST. INDIANAPOLIS, INDIANA 46268 USA

Copyright © 1962, 1967, and 1975 by Howard W. Sams & Co., Inc., Indianapolis, Indiana 46268

THIRD EDITION
SIXTH PRINTING—1980

All rights reserved. No part of this book shall be reproduced, stored in a retrieval system, or transmitted by any means, electronic, mechanical, photocopying, recording, or otherwise, without written permission from the publisher. No patent liability is assumed with respect to the use of the information contained herein. While every precaution has been taken in the preparation of this book, the publisher assumes no responsibility for errors or omissions. Neither is any liability assumed for damages resulting from the use of the information contained herein.

International Standard Book Number: 0-672-21127-0
Library of Congress Catalog Card Number: 74-33834

Printed in the United States of America.

Preface

Who would think of starting on a cross-country trip without first consulting a road map and plotting the route? Schematic diagrams and road maps have a lot in common—both show the "highways" from one point to another, and both use symbols to designate the various "landmarks." Yet, many students try to embark on a much more important trip—a career in electronics—without first learning how to properly read the "road maps" of the trade.

A simple key to the symbols, such as that included in the corner of most road maps, is not sufficient for electronic schematics. The highways, cities, rivers, etc., on the road map are familiar to everyone—you immediately have a picture of what is being represented. The components that make up an electronic circuit, however, are not as familiar. Before you can look at an electronic symbol and get a mental picture of its effect on the circuit, you must first know something about the component the symbol represents.

This book has been written to help you gain this needed knowledge of electronic components so that you can understand the symbols used to represent them in schematic diagrams. The many favorable comments and letters regarding the first two editions of this book indicate that this goal has been accomplished. In the years since the second edition of this book was introduced, there have been many changes in the electronics industry. The symbols have become more standardized, new components have been developed, and the use of others has declined. Hence, this third edition contains many new symbols and expanded explanations to keep in step with the latest developments. Logic circuits are now used to explain the operation of many IC circuits, so a new chapter on logic symbols has been added.

Only the theory considered necessary to understand the operation of a component and the reason for the symbol chosen to represent it is given. Once the purpose of a component and its construction are understood, you will see that its symbol is just as representative of the component as the line is of a highway.

The latter chapters of this book show how the components are combined to form circuits. Then, step-by-step, you follow signals through a schematic diagram of a radio receiver. The function of each stage and the meaning of the information on the schematic are explained.

This book has been written with the beginner or hobbyist in mind, but it will also serve as an invaluable reference for the technician.

DONALD E. HERRINGTON

To Thelma, Linda, and Bryan ...
... for their assistance and encouragement.

Contents

CHAPTER 1

Types of Electronic Diagrams

Many types of diagrams are needed to completely describe the operation and construction of electronic equipment. The most widely used, of course, is the *schematic* diagram—the subject of this book. A schematic is usually all that is required for analyzing, explaining, and servicing most circuits. But as we shall see, it cannot convey all the information about a piece of equipment; other types of diagrams are needed as well.

In this chapter we will discuss each of the different types, pointing out their particular advantages and disadvantages.

SCHEMATIC DIAGRAMS

The first questions the layman or student may ask when confronted by a schematic are "Why use all of these symbols? Couldn't the same information be given without resorting to the use of sign language? Is this just a conspiracy among people in electronics to keep us from learning the art?" The answer to the last two questions, as you will see, is definitely *no*.

Why Schematics and Symbols?

Symbols are used in electronic diagrams because experience has shown us that they are the quickest and easiest way to convey the needed information. Simple symbols are a form of electronic shorthand. With them a circuit can be sketched in a short time; and because the symbols are standard, they can be easily interpreted by other persons.

Use of symbols, or "sign language," enables all the necessary circuit information to be given on a relatively small drawing. Such a drawing is much easier to follow, or "read," than either an illustration or a photograph of the actual assembly of parts. Imagine the problems involved in trying to represent and analyze electronic equipment and components from "true-to-life" drawings! In addition, a drawing of the outside of a component does not show the internal construction of the unit.

If all the information contained in a schematic for even a simple radio were to be placed in written form, it would fill a book—yet, the schematic of the radio would easily fit on this page!

No, schematics are not meant to keep you in the dark about electronics. What the blueprint is to the architect or machinist, and the formula is to the chemist, the schematic is to those working with electronics. If you are just starting in electronics, study this book diligently. No matter what branch of this broad, fascinating field you eventually specialize in, a thorough knowledge of the symbols included in this book must be acquired first.

Information Conveyed by Schematics

Fig. 1-1 shows the schematic diagram of a typical amplifier used with a cassette tape recorder. Don't be concerned if it looks confusing to you now. In later chapters each symbol will be explained in detail. For the present we are only interested in what a schematic looks like and the kind of information it conveys.

First of all, the schematic shows all the electrical components and how they are connected to make up the circuit. The value (size) or type of each component is given, along with the colors of leads, the connections to each component, and other identifying marks.

Electrical measurements obtained at the various points, and the conditions under which they were taken, is also included in Fig. 1-1.

Component Identification

Another very important item included in Fig. 1-1 is a means of identifying each component. Notice the circled letter-and-number combinations beside each part. The letter signifies the type of component, and the number distinguishes it from all others of the same type. For instance, instead of saying "the 220-pF capacitor connected between the collector and base of the 2SC711 (G) audio amplifier," we can merely say "C412."

Other portions of the literature concerning a particular piece of equipment will also use these same reference letter-and-number designations. For instance, C412 may appear in a parts list which gives the part numbers and specifications for each component, and also on a photograph or drawing which shows its location. Thus, by using the same designation in all places to identify a component, there is less chance for an error to be made.

Unfortunately, all manufacturers do not designate a given component by the same code letters (or "class letter" or "call-outs" as they are sometimes called). However, they are fairly standard and usually only a few items will be different. The recommended letters appear in Table 1-1. In later chapters the other letters which will be encountered will be given.

Symbol Variation

Like the code letters, the symbols used by different companies also differ. The symbols for each component will be discussed in the following chapters, and where differences exist, the various ways of depicting a given item will be shown.

Organizations such as the Institute of Electrical and Electronic Engineers (IEEE) have adopted standard symbols which they hope the industry will use. Likewise, there are standards adopted by the American National Standards Institute (ANSI) and the military services, which, fortunately, are identical. The Electronic Industries Association (EIA) has also been instrumental in coordinating the efforts of various groups aimed at standardization of symbols.

The symbols used throughout the world are fairly standard. The International Electrotechnical Commission (IEC) recommends symbols to member countries throughout the world.

9

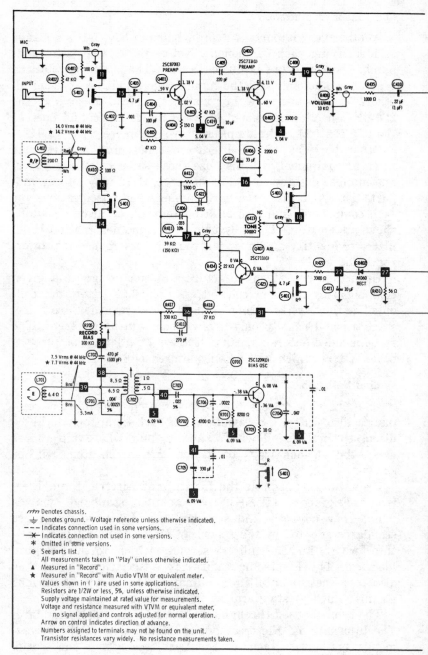

Fig. 1-1. Schematic of

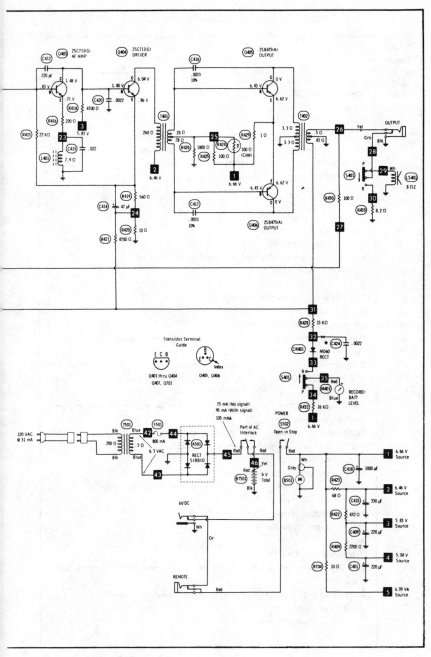

a typical cassette tape recorder.

Table 1-1. Recommended Code Letters

Code Letter	Designates
B	Blower, fan, motor, synchronous
BT	Battery, cell (battery), cell (solar)
C	Capacitor
CB	Circuit breaker
CR	Current regulator (semiconductor), crystal detector, diode (semiconductor, all types), metallic rectifier, thyristor (semiconductor diode type), semiconductor switch, semiconductor rectifier, varactor
DS	Bell, buzzer, lamp (all types), siren, telegraph sounder
E	Antenna, lightning arrester, shield
F	Fuse
G	Generator, chopper, magneto
HR	Heater, heating lamp, heating resistor
HS	Handset, operator's set
HT	Earphone, headset, telephone or hearing aid receiver
J	Connector (receptacle), jack
K	Relay
L	Coil (all types), inductor, solenoid
LS	Horn, speaker
M	Clock, gage, instrument, motor, timer
MG	Dynamotor, inverters (motor-generator), motor generator
MK	Microphone, telephone transmitter
P	Connector (plug), plug, disconnecting device
PU	Magnetic head (erase, record, play), head (sound record or reproduce), phono pickup
Q	Transistor, semiconductor controlled rectifier or switch, thyristor (semiconductor triode)
R	Potentiometer, resistor, rheostat, instrument or relay shunt
RT	Resistance lamp, thermal or current regulating resistor, ballast lamp or tube, thermistor
RV	Resistor (voltage sensitive), varistor
S	Switch (all types) telegraph key, thermal cutout, thermostat
T	Transformer (all types)
TB	Terminal board, terminal strip, test block
TC	Thermocouple, thermopile
TP	Testpoint
U	Microcircuit, integrated circuit
V	Cell (light sensitive, photoemissive, or photo sensitive), electron tube, thyratron
VR	Breakdown diode, voltage regulator (except electron tube)
W	Cable, wire, busbar
X	Fuse holder, lamp holder, socket
Y	Crystal unit

Most ANSI and IEEE symbols agree with these recommendations. Thus, once the symbols given in this book are mastered, you should have no problem understanding a schematic from anywhere—except, of course, foreign terms will be used on it. The differences between two U.S. schematics may be greater than between a U.S. and a foreign schematic.

Fortunately, the differences in the symbol used by various companies to depict a component are not so great as in previous years. Differences still exist, however, so in the later chapters of this book, the symbols used by various companies will be shown. In general, the weight of a line or minor differences do not change the meaning of a symbol. In fact, the symbol can be completely reversed; that is, two symbols can be the mirror image of each other and still have the same meaning.

Most of the differences in the symbols chosen stem from differences in the type of drafting and the method of laying out the circuit; they have no effect on the meaning. Schematics may be hand sketched, drawn with ink and a symbol guide, produced using preprinted symbols, or even prepared by a machine having a keyboard similar to that of a typesetting machine. Therefore, minor differences are inevitable.

BLOCK DIAGRAMS

The block diagram (Fig. 1-2) is also often used in electronics. Even though it does not provide as much information as the schematic, it nevertheless is very useful because it is easier to interpret for certain limited purposes.

The principal use of the block diagram is to show the overall operation of the circuit—in other words, the interrelationships of the various stages. Additional blocks will often be included to provide other information. The diagram in Fig. 1-2 is "read" by starting with the block farthest to the top left, labeled "1st Preamp," then following the arrows through the 2nd Preamp, the af amplifier, the driver, the audio-output tubes, and ending at the speaker. Either the microphone or the playback head is connected to the 1st Preamp by the switch, depending on whether you intend to record or play a tape. During record, the signal is coupled back to the automatic level stage to automatically adjust the gain of the 2nd Preamp so the proper level signal will be applied to the record head.

(Although not shown, the speaker is disconnected during record.) The block labeled "Power Supply" furnishes all the other blocks with the necessary power.

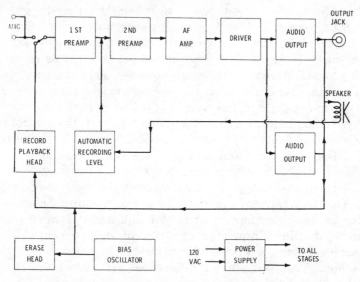

Fig. 1-2. Block diagram of the cassette tape recorder pictured in Fig. 1-1.

In summary, a block diagram shows the path of the signal through the circuit, and the function of each stage. It does not furnish any information about the type of connections or components; hence, it has only limited use. But for only a brief look at the overall operation and functions of a unit, the block diagram is the simplest and easiest to follow.

CHASSIS-LAYOUT DIAGRAMS

A third type of diagram appears in Fig. 1-3. Often called a *transistor placement chart,* it shows the physical locations of the major components. A placement chart is extremely useful for more complicated pieces of equipment such as television receivers. As more and more components are added, the task of determining just which tube or transistor fulfills a given function becomes more difficult. With a diagram like the one in Fig. 1-3, locating a certain tube or transistor is greatly simplified.

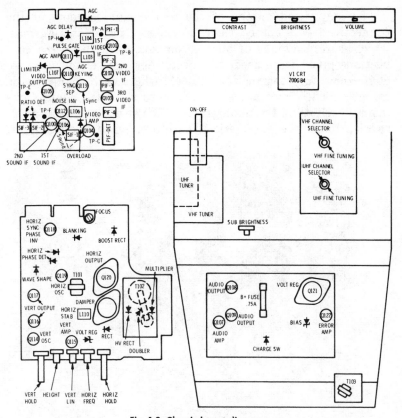

Fig. 1-3. Chassis layout diagram.

PHOTOGRAPHS AND PICTORIAL DIAGRAMS

The schematic diagram has one important limitation—it does not show the actual physical location of the individual components. Even though it shows all electrical connections correctly, a particular part will often be located some distance away from its associated components on the chassis. Such a part could be located by tracing through the circuit—but the easiest way is to use a photograph with each part labeled, as shown in Fig. 1-4.

In the photograph, parts located beneath other components cannot be seen. In such a case the line pointing out the hidden component will stop on the object hiding it, and the arrowhead will be omitted to signify that it is the part underneath.

The only disadvantage of the photograph is some of the connections will not be clear. Formerly, pictorial diagrams, which were drawings of all the components with all the connections given were used. However, they are seldom used today, except for construction projects where each connection is essential. The pictorial can be drawn to show the connections more clearly than the photograph. But neither can show them as clearly as the schematic. Therefore, when the electrical

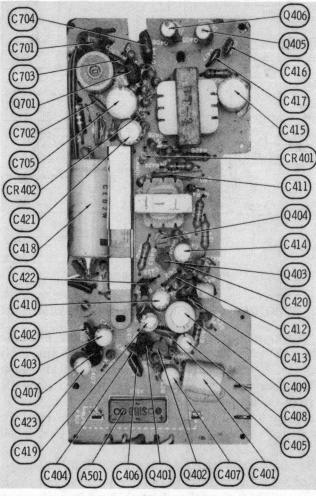

Fig. 1-4. Photograph of the cassette tape recorder chassis of Fig. 1-1, showing component location.

connections are of primary interest, a schematic is used; but when only the physical location of a given part is desired, a pictorial or photograph is of greater value.

MECHANICAL DIAGRAMS

One important function ignored by the diagrams discussed previously is mechanical action or connections. Let us look at a few of the more common types of diagrams used for this purpose.

Dial-Cord Stringing

Replacing a dial cord on a receiver can be a most difficult and, in some instances, an impossible task without proper instruction. Fig. 1-5 shows a diagram prepared to provide the

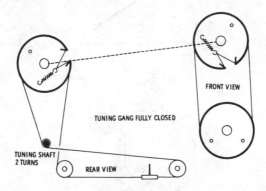

Fig. 1-5. A dial-cord stringing diagram.

necessary information to make the job comparatively easy. Without such help, hours might be spent trying to determine the correct method, especially for more complicated arrangements.

"Exploded" Views

For certain pieces of electrical and electronic equipment the operation of which is largely mechanical (such as record changers and tape recorders), the interrelationship between parts can best be shown on a diagram known as an "exploded" view. Fig. 1-6 shows such a diagram. Each part is "exploded" from its normal position. The relationship of each part with

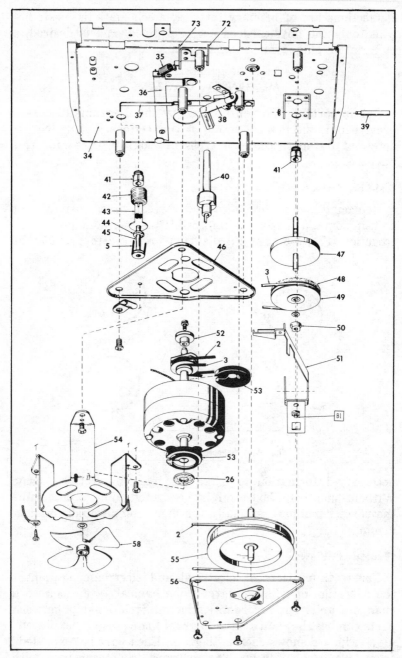

Fig. 1-6. An exploded view.

respect to all the others is maintained, however, and the dashed lines point to their correct position in the assembly. Each part is identified by a number. By referring to this number in the parts list, the name and description of the item, as well as the manufacturer's part number (if a replacement must be ordered), can be determined.

REVIEW OF FUNDAMENTALS

While this book is not intended as a text on basic electronic theory, a brief review of fundamental principles may be of value, especially in understanding some of the terms used in the chapters to follow.

Electron Theory

All matter is made up of atoms. The atom is the smallest particle which retains all the characteristics of the 100+ known elements that are combined to form all material. The atom, in turn, is made up of smaller particles, called electrons and protons (plus some other particles not important to our discussion). The proton has a minute positive charge and is located in the center of the atom (called the nucleus) along with other particles.

The electrons, having a negative charge, then orbit around this nucleus. Thus, the nucleus could be likened to the sun and the electrons to the planets orbiting around it. However, unlike the planets, each of which has a separate orbit, more than one electron will normally follow the same orbit in the atom. For example, Fig. 1-7 compares a helium atom with a copper atom. Since protons have a positive charge, they are represented by the + sign in the center, while the electrons having a negative charge are shown orbiting around the nucleus. Notice helium has two protons and two electrons in the same orbit (called a shell). Copper has 29 protons in the nucleus and 29 orbiting electrons arranged in 4 orbits or shells.

Since like electrical charges repel each other and unlike electrical charges attract, electrons in Fig. 1-7 would be attracted to the protons in the nucleus, but the centrifugal force of the orbiting electrons is sufficient enough to counteract the effect of the opposing charges. Thus, each electron stays in place orbiting the nucleus. In an atom such as copper (Fig. 1-7B), where there is a single electron in the outer shell, it is possible to cause this electron to move from its outer orbit to the outer orbit of an adjacent atom. The electron formerly at this point is then "bumped" to the next adjacent atom and so on. This is shown in simplified form in Fig. 1-8. As the electron enters at the left, another electron moves to the center atom, and then

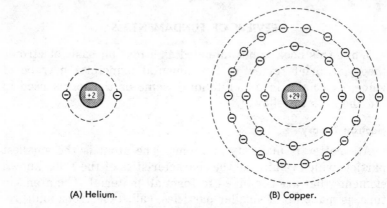

(A) Helium.   (B) Copper.

Fig. 1-7. Comparison of helium and copper atoms.

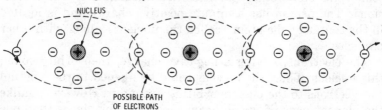

Fig. 1-8. Simplified concept of electron flow.

another electron moves to the right atom. Thus, in effect we have a flow of electrons through the material. An electric current is nothing but a flow of electrons. This flow is at the speed of light in free space, and just slightly slower in other materials; so, for all practical purposes, the flow is instantaneous.

The construction of some atoms is such that electrons will not flow as readily from one atom to the next. When electrons flow readily as in our example, the material is called a *conductor*. When electrons will not flow, the material is called an *insulator*.

The flow of electrons can be controlled in several ways. For example, when an electric switch is opened the flow of electrons through the wire is stopped. Electrons can be caused to do much more than flow through a wire, however. By proper manipulation of the flow of this tiny electron, the entire field of electricity and electronics is made possible. It is difficult to say where electricity ends and electronics begins, but electronics is normally considered to encompass the entire field of controlling the flow of electrons through the use of tubes and semiconductor devices, such as transistors. Thus, radio, television, radar, and most of our modern conveniences are made possible through controlling the flow of this tiny negative charge in an atom.

Alternating and Direct Current

The rate at which electrons flow is defined as current. Thus, if relatively few electrons flow, we have a small current; if more flow we have a larger current. etc. Before any electrons can flow, however, there must be some force to cause it. This force is called *electromotive force* (abbreviated emf), or *voltage*. This force, which can be likened to pressure, can be produced in many ways. Through chemical action, a battery produces voltage; through mechanical action, an alternator produces voltage.

Recall that an electron has a negative charge. Thus, if a material can be made to have more than the normal amount of electrons, it is said to have a negative voltage. Likewise, if a material can be made to have less than the normal amount of electrons, it can be said to have a positive voltage. This is what happens in the flashlight cell shown in Fig. 1-9. Through chemical reaction, an excess of electrons is created at the outside covering (bottom) of the cell. Likewise a deficiency of electrons is created at the center terminal (top). If a wire is connected between these two points, electrons will flow through

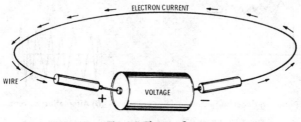

Fig. 1-9. Electron flow.

the wire from the negative to the positive terminal. Recall that like charges repel; therefore, the concentration of electrons at the bottom of the battery will repel those electrons adjacent to it in the wire, and the chain reaction is started. Since the positive post at the top has a deficiency of electrons, they are attracted to this point because unlike charges attract. This flow of electrons (current) will continue until the two points equalize.

A circuit like Fig. 1-9 can serve no useful purpose; it will only discharge the battery. However, if instead of a wire other devices are connected between these two points, the electrons can be made to do work while moving from one point to another. For example, if a light bulb is connected instead of the wire, the electrons will heat the wire in the bulb and produce light as they race toward the positive terminal.

The current produced in Fig. 1-9 is said to be direct current because it flows in only one direction through the wire. Such a current is diagrammed as shown in Fig. 1-10A. The instant the wire is touched to the two terminals, current starts flowing; this is represented by the line rising up and then extending in a straight line to the right. The vertical axis—the distance from the center (zero point) to the top—represents the *amount* of current, and the horizontal axis represents *time*.

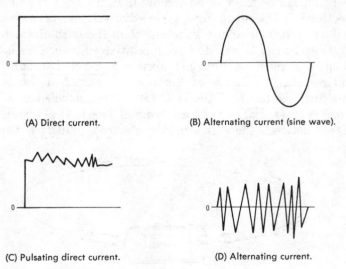

(A) Direct current.

(B) Alternating current (sine wave).

(C) Pulsating direct current.

(D) Alternating current.

Fig. 1-10. Alternating and direct current waveforms.

Now, suppose we took the two probes on the ends of the wire in Fig. 1-9 and reversed them so they were connected to opposite terminals of the battery. The electrons would now flow in the opposite direction through the wire. If we continued to reverse the leads, you can see that current through the wire would first flow in one direction and then in the other. Of course, this method of changing the direction of electron flow (current) is not practical, but in mechanical devices such as the ordinary alternator in a car, this is what happens. At a given terminal the voltage (potential) will first be negative and then positive. Then, when it is positive, electrons will flow toward the terminal, and when it is negative, electrons will flow away from the terminal and toward the opposite terminal. This is alternating current and is diagrammed as shown in Fig. 1-10B. Here, the current builds up to a peak, then decreases and flows in the opposite direction to a similar peak and back to zero. The waveform shown in Fig. 1-10D is a special type of alternating current and is called a *sine wave*. The power supplied by the power companies is of this type.

Most of the currents encountered in electronic equipment do not follow either of the patterns shown in Fig. 1-10A and B. Instead, they will usually be more like the ones in Fig. 1-10C or D. Notice that the waveform in Fig. 1-10C is direct current because it extends in only one direction from the zero line. However, it is not steady; hence it is called a *pulsating direct current*. The waveform in Fig. 1-10D is alternating current, since it extends both above and below the zero line, but it also varies and does not follow the sine-wave pattern.

While the waveforms in Fig. 1-10 have been described as current waveforms, they also represent the voltage present at a given point. When used to represent voltage, that portion above the zero line represents a positive voltage, while the portion below the line is a negative voltage. Thus, in Fig. 1-10A, a steady positive voltage is represented, while in Fig. 1-10C, the voltage is still positive but it varies. In Fig. 1-10B, the voltage first goes positive and then decreases in value to zero and on to a negative value and back to zero. The same is true of Fig. 1-10D, except here the changes follow a different pattern. The shape of the waveform will be the same whether it represents voltage or the resulting current.

The important points to remember about the electron-flow concept can be summarized as follows:

1. Electrons are negatively charged particles.
2. Protons are positively charged particles.
3. Like charges repel and unlike charges attract.
4. When a path is provided, electrons will move from an area having an excess of electrons to one having a deficiency of electrons.
5. When electrons flow in only one direction, direct current (dc) is present.
6. When electrons flow in one direction and then in the opposite direction, alternating current (ac) is present.
7. Electronics is the science of controlling the flow of electrons in such a manner as to produce a desired result, usually with circuitry utilizing vacuum tubes or semiconductor devices.

Now, with the foregoing concepts in mind, the various components used in electronics can be discussed. The effect each will have on the flow of electrons through it and the symbols used to represent each device on schematic diagrams will be given in the following chapters.

QUESTIONS

1. What is a schematic?
2. How are the individual components on a schematic identified?
3. What information does a block diagram convey?
4. What does a pictorial diagram or photograph show that a schematic cannot?
5. What are the advantages of a photograph over a pictorial diagram?
6. Why are schematics used?
7. How are record-changer mechanisms usually shown in service literature?
8. What does a chassis-layout diagram show?
9. Name two types of mechanical diagrams.
10. What is the most popular type of electronic diagram?

CHAPTER 2

Resistors

The resistor is probably the most common of all electronic components. Every radio, television, or other piece of electronic equipment will contain several such units.

WHAT IS A RESISTOR?

In electronic circuits, resistors perform exactly the function their name implies—they *resist*, or oppose, the flow of electrons. In other words, a resistor might be said to introduce *electrical friction*. Every electrical component contains a certain amount of resistance, even a piece of ordinary wire. But to obtain the amount of resistance provided by just one resistor might require many feet, or even miles, of wire. By using resistors, however, practically any amount of resistance can be contained in a small, compact unit.

Resistor Ratings

Two types of ratings, or values, are specified for a resistor. The first is the electrical value—how much resistance it will introduce into the circuit. This value is given in *ohms,* the unit of resistance measurement. Thus, if a resistor has a value of 1000 ohms it will introduce an electrical opposition of 1000 units to the flow of electrons in a circuit.

This opposition reduces the amount of current flow in a given circuit. By proper selection of resistor value it is possible to obtain the exact amount of current required. Also, when current flows through a resistor a voltage is developed across it. This means that the voltage at one end of a resistor will be lower than at the other end by an amount proportional to the current flow through it. Mathematically, this is expressed as:

$$E = I \times R$$

where,
   E is the voltage in volts,
   I is the current in amperes,
   R is the resistance in ohms.

Thus, the two most important functions of a resistor are: (1) to limit current flow, and (2) to provide a voltage difference.

The second value given in rating a resistor is the *wattage* —how much current can flow through it without causing damage. The unit of measurement is the *watt,* and in general, the larger the physical size of the resistor the higher its wattage rating will be. Common ratings are ¼, ½, 1, 2, and 5 watts or more. Regardless of this wattage rating, however, the resistance of the unit does not change. Thus, a ½-watt resistor could be replaced by a 1-watt or even a 5-watt unit. If, however, a 1-watt resistor was replaced by a ½-watt unit, the latter might burn out.

Abbreviations and symbols are often used in designating resistor values. For example, the Greek letter *omega* (Ω) is usually employed in the place of the word "ohm." Thus, instead of writing out *100 ohms,* it is usually written as 100 Ω. The letter *K* is used to designate 1000 and *meg* or *megohm* stands for "one million ohms." The *K* is sometimes followed by the Ω sign—at other times it is understood and hence omitted. Thus *100,000* ohms, *100 KΩ,* and *100K* all mean the same. *Watts* is usually indicated by the capital letter *W.* For instance, *1W* signifies a 1-watt unit.

FIXED RESISTORS

The fixed resistor is the simplest type. "Fixed" means the unit is constructed in such a way that its ohmic value cannot be varied. Fig. 2-1 shows some examples of this type, each having a certain value determined by the composition and amount of the material from which it is made.

Many fixed resistors are made of a carbon composition—hence the name *carbon resistor*. Others, especially those for high-wattage applications, use a special high-resistance wire

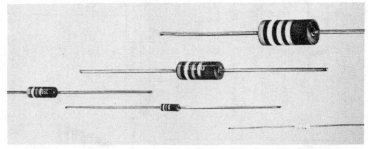

Courtesy Ohmite Mfg. Co.

Fig. 2-1. An assortment of carbon resistors.

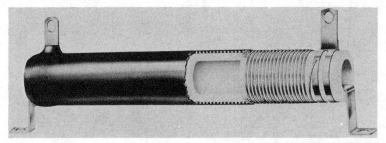

Courtesy Ohmite Mfg. Co.

Fig. 2-2. Construction of a wirewound resistor.

wound on a ceramic or other insulating core. This assembly is then covered with a vitreous-enamel protective coating. A cutaway view of this type is shown in Fig. 2-2.

Another type of resistor developed for certain applications is the *metallized* unit. It is constructed by depositing a thin coating of a resistive material onto a glass rod.

A fixed resistor is usually marked in some way to show the value of the unit. This is most often done by a system of *color coding*. Chart 2-1 shows the code used for carbon resistors—the most common method shown at A and the older methods at B and C. In the first method the two bands nearest the end designate the first two figures of the ohmic value, and the third

Chart 2-1. Resistor Codes

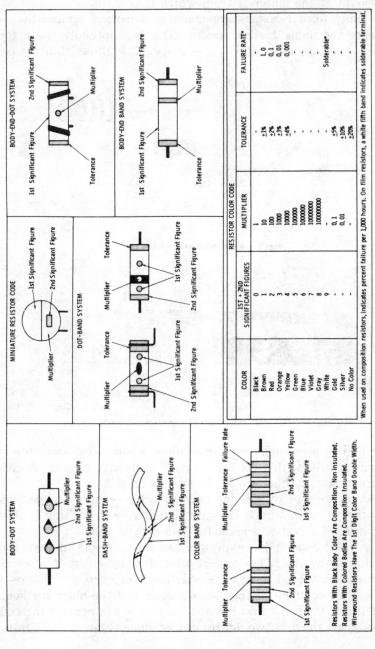

RESISTOR COLOR CODE

COLOR	1ST + 2ND SIGNIFICANT FIGURES	MULTIPLIER	TOLERANCE	FAILURE RATE*
Black	0	1	-	-
Brown	1	10	±1%	1.0
Red	2	100	±2%	0.1
Orange	3	1000	±3%	0.01
Yellow	4	10000	±4%	0.001
Green	5	100000	-	-
Blue	6	1000000	-	-
Violet	7	10000000	-	-
Gray	8	100000000	-	-
White	9	-	-	Solderable*
Gold	-	0.1	±5%	-
Silver	-	0.01	±10%	-
No Color	-	-	±20%	-

*When used on composition resistors, indicates percent failure per 1,000 hours. On film resistors, a white fifth band indicates solderable terminal.

Resistors With Black Body Color Are Composition, Non Insulated.
Resistors With Colored Bodies Are Composition Insulated.
Wirewound Resistors Have The 1st Digit Color Band Double Width.

band the number of zeros to be added to arrive at the correct value.

Thus, a resistor having a yellow, violet, and red band has a value of 4700 ohms. If a fourth band is present, it will signify how close the resistance is to the indicated value. This is known as the *tolerance*. It is impossible to make each resistor to have the *exact* resistance indicated by its color bands, so certain standard values have been adopted. All resistors which fall within the required percentage of this standard are coded with this value. If no fourth band is present, the resistor is within 20% of the indicated value. A silver band designates 10%, and a gold band, 5% tolerance. Other tolerances are given in Chart 2-1.

Other resistors, especially the wirewound type, will have the value stamped on the side. The wattage rating will often be included also. Some of the newer resistors are so tiny there is no room for a complete color code. In resistors of this type a special code must be devised; for example, a single red dot might designate a 2200-ohm resistor.

The schematic symbols for designating fixed resistors are shown in Fig. 2-3. The symbol at A is the most common—

A   B   C

Fig. 2-3. Fixed-resistor symbols.

those at B and C will seldom be encountered. When the symbol at B is used, the value of the resistor will usually be placed inside the box. It is a popular symbol on foreign schematics.

Like the resistance symbol, the code letter used to designate a resistance is also more standardized than most of the others. All American manufacturers designate a fixed resistor by the letter *R*.

TAPPED AND ADJUSTABLE RESISTORS

A fixed resistor will sometimes have a tap or connection at some point along the resistance material. Fig. 2-4 shows the symbols used for such a unit. The symbol at A is used almost exclusively and is the same as for a fixed resistor except for the line connected to the zigzag portion. If there are two taps, another line is added as shown at B. A dot is sometimes added at the point where the line connects to the regular resistor symbol as shown at C. The resistance value of the entire unit, as well as the value at the tapped point, is given for this type of resistor. The symbol at D in Fig. 2-4 is used by companies which employ the symbol at B in Fig. 2-3.

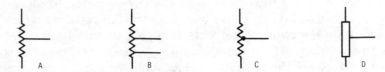

Fig. 2-4. Tapped resistor symbols.

Most tapped resistors are wirewound units with a separate terminal for each tap. In some units the tap is made adjustable by making it in the form of a band around the resistor. The resistance wire is left exposed along one side of the unit and this band makes contact at the desired point. It is then secured by tightening a screw. Once set, the value of such resistors is seldom changed.

The same symbols shown in Fig. 2-4 are sometimes used to designate these types of adjustable resistors. An arrowhead, however, is usually added at the connection point, as shown in Fig. 2-5. Like the fixed resistor, R is the code letter always used for both tapped and adjustable resistors.

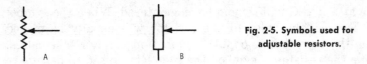

Fig. 2-5. Symbols used for adjustable resistors.

VARIABLE RESISTORS

A resistor which can be continuously varied in value is often needed. In lighting and other power circuits, such a resistor is usually called a *rheostat*. Rheostats almost always consist of a wirewound resistance element arranged in a circle with a sliding contact (as shown in Fig. 2-6) with connections to one end of the resistance element and the sliding arm.

Another type of continuously variable resistor is called a *potentiometer*. In appearance it is usually very similar to the

Courtesy P. R. Mallory & Co., Inc.

Fig. 2-6. An assortment of rheostats.

rheostat and can have a wirewound, carbon, or other composition resistance element. The potentiometer has connections to each end of the resistance element and the sliding arm or it can have connections to one end of the resistance element and the sliding arm and be used as a rheostat. Fig. 2-7 shows an example of potentiometers that can be adjusted with a screwdriver to obtain the desired resistance. The ones in Fig. 2-7A have a circular resistance element similar to the rheostat of Fig. 2-6. The potentiometer of Fig. 2-7B has a wire element wound around a cylindrical shaft for precision adjustments.

The potentiometers of Fig. 2-8 are designed to be adjusted by a knob attached to the shaft. Those at A and B are the type of controls used to adjust the volume, contrast, brightness, and other items on entertainment equipment. The one at C is a precision potentiometer requiring 10 turns of the shaft to move the arm from one end of the element to the other.

The most common variable-resistor symbols are those labeled A and B in Fig. 2-9. These are alike with the exception that no connection is shown at one end in B. This does not necessarily mean the unit has only two connections. If the third terminal is not used—as is often the case—it is not shown. The symbols at C and D also designate either a rheostat or potentiometer with only two terminals used. Here, the arrow through the symbol signifies it is adjustable. Two variations of ways to show the variable arm are shown at E and F. Others will also be encountered but the basic symbol is virtually the same on all. The symbols at G and H represent a preset adjustment (usually a screwdriver adjustment). This symbol is for the potentiometers of Fig. 2-7. Quite often, however, the other symbols are used to represent this type of variable resistor.

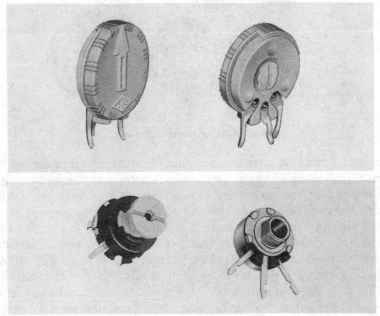

Courtesy Centralab, Electronics Div. of Globe-Union, Inc.

(A) Circular resistance elements.

(B) Cylindrical resistance element.

Courtesy Clarostat Mfg. Co., Inc.

Fig. 2-7. Screwdriver adjusted potentiometers.

Courtesy Clarostat Mfg. Co., Inc.

Fig. 2-8. Shaft-adjusted potentiometers.

The symbol at I signifies a potentiometer that has a tap to provide an additional fixed connection. Some units are made in such a way that the sliding contact will not move beyond a certain point on the element. This always leaves some resistance between the arm and one end of the potentiometer. The symbol for this type is shown at J; the line drawn across the symbol indicates the limit to which the movable contact will travel.

The value of a variable resistance may not always be stamped on the unit. The manufacturer's part number is often the only information given. To find the value, refer to the schematic, parts list, or manufacturer's catalog.

The most popular code letter for designating a variable resistor is R. Some manufacturers, however, prefer the letter P (for potentiometer) or VR (for variable resistor).

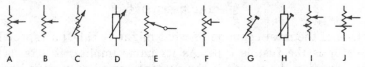

Fig. 2-9. Continuously variable rheostat or potentiometer symbols.

Two potentiometers are sometimes constructed in one assembly, one unit being mounted behind the other. The shaft for one is hollow, allowing the shaft of the other unit to pass through it. This arrangement is quite common for certain tv controls; the operation is the same as for two separate units. The same code letter and number will often designate both units, with an A and B added to distinguish between them—such as R1A and R1B.

A switch may also be included on the back of potentiometers. Fig. 2-10 shows an exploded view of such a control. The outer shaft is used to vary the front potentiometer. The inner shaft which varies the resistance of the rear potentiometer also actuates the switch. Electrically, however, there is no connection between the sections.

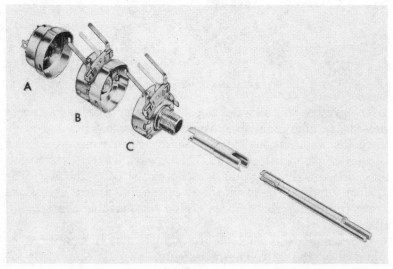

Courtesy Centralab, Electronics Div. of Globe-Union, Inc.

Fig. 2-10. Exploded view of a two-section potentiometer and on-off switch: (A) Switch, (B) Rear potentiometer, (C) Front potentiometer.

SPECIAL RESISTORS

One of the most common of what might be called a "special" resistor is the fusible type. As its name implies, it acts as a fuse, opening the circuit if the current exceeds a certain limit.

This protects expensive components against damage, and only a relatively inexpensive resistor must be replaced. Such units often are made to plug into a socket on the chassis, making replacement as simple as changing a tube. The symbols for such components are given in Fig. 2-11. Notice that the familiar resistor symbol is still used, but with the plug-in arrangement indicated by an arrowhead or other appropriate designation. The fact that the unit is fusible is usually indicated by a notation near the symbol. Occasionally the conventional fuse symbol (see Chapter 8) is used for a fusible resistor.

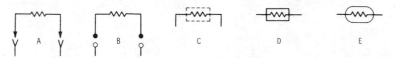

Fig. 2-11. Fusible-resistor symbols.

Often there is a need for a special type of resistor which will vary in value when the conditions surrounding it or conditions in the circuit change. Many of these units are actually semiconductor devices (to be discussed in a later chapter); however, since they are used in a circuit to supply resistance, they will be given in this chapter.

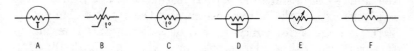

Fig. 2-12. Thermister symbols.

As the temperature of a common carbon resistor rises because of heat from surrounding components or from its own internal electron flow, the resistance of the resistor increases. To forestall this change, the composition of the resistor is altered to cause its resistance to decrease when the temperature increases. In fact, the change in resistance can be made to either increase, decrease, or remain constant regardless of the direction of temperature change (within limits, of course). These units are known as *temperature-compensating resistors, thermistors,* or *thermal resistors* (Fig. 2-12). If the resistance decreases as the temperature rises, they are said to have a *negative temperature coefficient* (NTC); if it increases, they have a *positive temperature coefficient* (PTC). The abbreviation signifying the type is usually placed beside the symbol. Thermistors can also be used as the sensing element of electronic thermometers.

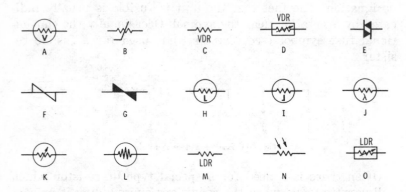

Fig. 2-13. Voltage- and light-dependent resistor symbols.

Resistors are also available which vary in value according to the current through them or the voltage present in the circuit. Others vary in value when light strikes them. Often the same symbol shown at A or B in Fig. 2-12 is used for these resistors except the letter designating the type is changed to *V* for voltage, *I* for current, or *L* or λ for light. Other manufacturers use different symbols, however. In Fig. 2-13, symbols A through G are for voltage-dependent resistors; those in H through O are for light-dependent resistors.

The letter *R* is usually employed as the code letter for voltage-, current-, temperature-, or light-dependent resistors. However, *RT* may be used for temperature-dependent resistors and *RV* for voltage-dependent resistors. In addition, *D* or *CR* is sometimes used as the code letter for semiconductor-type resistors.

REVIEW QUESTIONS

1. What is the unit of measurement for the amount of resistance?

2. What are the two main purposes of resistors?
3. What is resistance?
4. What Greek letter is used as the symbol for ohm?
5. What is a potentiometer?
6. What code letter is used for resistors?
7. What is the value of a resistor with red, violet, and orange bands?
8. What is a negative temperature-coefficient resistor?
9. Draw the symbol for a fixed resistor.
10. Draw the symbol for a tapped potentiometer.

CHAPTER 3

Capacitors

Like the resistor discussed in the previous chapter, the capacitor is found in nearly every electronic circuit. The term "condenser" was formerly used when referring to this unit, and will still be heard occasionally, but "capacitor" is now more universally accepted.

WHAT IS A CAPACITOR?

Basically, a capacitor is a device consisting of two plates of a conducting material separated by an insulator (Fig. 3-1). This arrangement gives it the property of being able to store and release electrons as dictated by the external conditions affecting it. This storage and release is more commonly called *charge* and *discharge*.

Electrons will not actually flow through the insulating material; however, when a large quantity of electrons are stored on one plate, making it more negative, the electrons on the opposite plate will be repelled, causing an electron flow away from this plate. Therefore, if an ac signal is connected to one plate, causing a build-up and depletion of electrons on this plate, a similar effect will occur on the opposite plate even though no electrons actually flow through the insulating material (called the *dielectric*).

If dc is connected to one plate of the capacitor, it will act as an open circuit. The amount of electrons does not vary on the plate connected to the dc; therefore, there will be no movement of electrons to or from the second plate. The property by which a capacitor transfers an ac signal from one plate to another is called *coupling;* the property of acting as an open circuit to dc is called *blocking.*

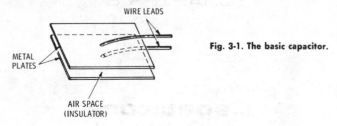

Fig. 3-1. The basic capacitor.

WIRE LEADS

METAL
PLATES

AIR SPACE
(INSULATOR)

CAPACITANCE

The property by which a capacitor is able to store electrons is called *capacitance.* The larger the plate area, the more electrons can be stored and hence the larger the capacitance. The unit of capacitance measurement is the *farad.* Since this unit is too large for ordinary work, the *microfarad* (one millionth of a farad) is more common. Microfarad is abbreviated μF. (The symbol μ is the Greek letter *mu,* the abbreviation for one millionth.) A still smaller unit, the picofarad (abbreviated pF) is sometimes encountered. This unit is equal to one millionth of one millionth of a farad, or one millionth of a microfarad. In other words:

$$1 \text{ pF} = .000001 \ \mu\text{F} = .000000000001 \text{ farad}$$

The term micromicrofarad (mmf, mmfd, $\mu\mu$f, or $\mu\mu$fd) was formerly used for picofarad and is still encountered, but it is largely being replaced by the term "picofarad."

FIXED CAPACITORS

The capacitor shown in Fig. 3-1 is too large physically to be practical for most uses. If another insulating material is used instead of air, and if the plates are then rolled instead of lying flat, the unit can be made to occupy a much smaller space. This method is shown in Fig. 3-2. This assembly can then be enclosed in plastic or wax-impregnated paper.

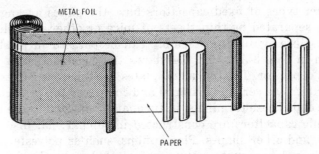

Fig. 3-2. Paper capacitor construction.

Courtesy Cornell-Dubilier Electric Corp.

(A) Molded mica.

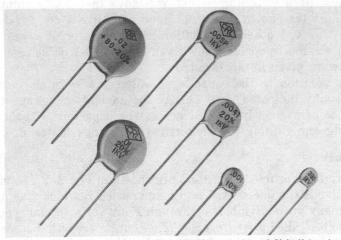

Courtesy Centralab, Electronics Div. of Globe-Union, Inc.

(B) Disc ceramic.

Fig. 3-3. Fixed capacitors.

Other types of fixed capacitors have the plates arranged in layers separated by thin sheets of mica or other suitable material. Here again, the assembly can be encased in plastic as shown in Fig. 3-3A. Fig. 3-4 shows the construction of a ceramic capacitor. The two metal plates (in this case, silver) are separated by a ceramic material and connected to the terminals at the end. These terminals, in turn, are connected to the leads. Ceramic capacitors are constructed in tubular, flat disc (Fig. 3-3B), and other shapes. Plastic films, such as polyester, polystyrene, polycarbonate, polytetrafluorethylene, and polypropylene are used as dielectrics in capacitors. All, however, have the same basic characteristic—conducting surfaces separated by an insulator.

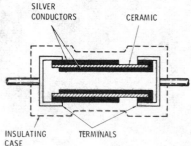

Fig. 3-4. Ceramic-capacitor construction.

SILVER CONDUCTORS

CERAMIC

INSULATING CASE

TERMINALS

Color Codes

Most fixed capacitors either will have their value stamped on them (as shown in Fig. 3-3) or will have a color code to give this and other information. Several different codes are used, the most popular being given in Chart 3-1. (The capacity is always given in picofarads.)

In addition to the capacitance value, the working voltage is usually indicated also. This is the amount of voltage that can be continuously applied across the capacitor without its arcing and ruining the dielectric (insulating) material.

Symbols

Symbols for fixed capacitors are shown in Fig. 3-5. The most popular is the one at A, having superseded B which was used for many years. Symbols C through F are for a special type of capacitor called a *feedthrough*. These units are either inserted through a hole in the chassis and soldered in place, or are screwed into a threaded hole. Typical feedthrough capacitors are pictured in Fig. 3-6.

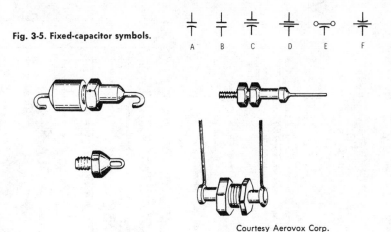

Fig. 3-5. Fixed-capacitor symbols.

A   B   C   D   E   F

Courtesy Aerovox Corp.

Fig. 3-6. Four types of feedthrough capacitors.

Temperature Coefficient

Another rating often included in the color code is the *temperature coefficient*. Like resistors, capacitors often change in value when heated. To compensate for this, they can be manufactured so that their value will not vary at all, or will increase or decrease by predetermined amounts as the temperature changes. The temperature coefficient designates the amount of change in parts-per-million-per-degree Celsius (centigrade). An *N* or a minus sign (−) indicates a decrease in capacitance, and a *P* or a plus sign (+), an increase.

ELECTROLYTIC CAPACITORS

Examples of another type of capacitor are shown in Fig. 3-7. These are called *electrolytics* because one plate consists of a moist substance called an *electrolyte*. Certain metals—aluminum and tantalum are the most common—will have a thin oxide film form on their surface when immersed in an electrolyte. This oxide film becomes the insulation or dielectric between the metal plate and the electrolyte which serves as the other plate. Such capacitors are characterized by a high capacitance in comparison to their size.

Unlike other capacitors, electrolytics must usually be connected in the correct polarity. That is, the positive terminal

Chart 3-1. Capacitor

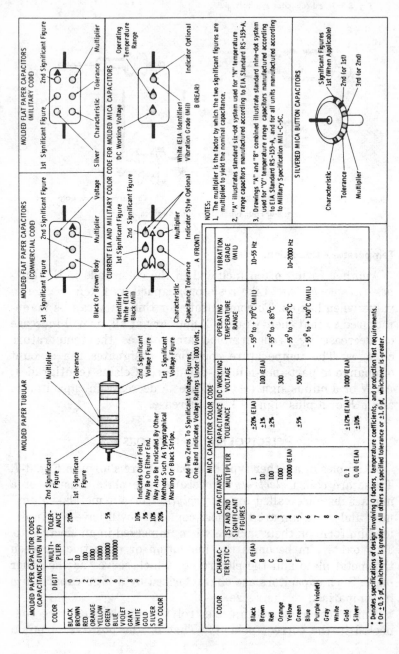

Outline Drawings and Color Codes

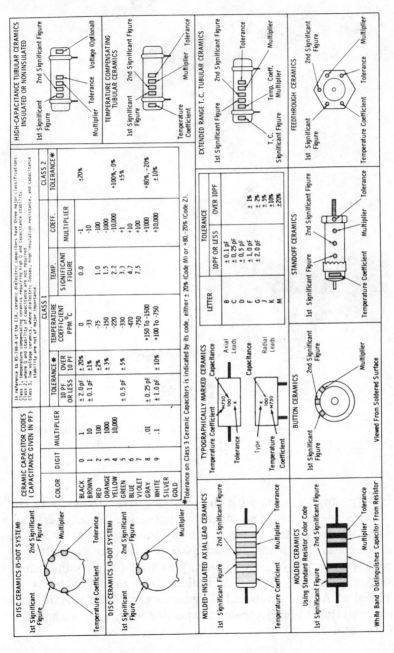

In reference to RS-198-A of the EIA, ceramic dielectric capacitors have three major classifications. Class 1, temperature compensating ceramics requiring high Q and capacitance stability. Class 2, where Q and stability of capacitance are not required. Class 3, low voltage ceramics, where dielectric losses, high insulation resistance, and capacitance stability are not of major importance.

CERAMIC CAPACITOR CODES (CAPACITANCE GIVEN IN PF)

			CLASS 1					CLASS 2
COLOR	DIGIT	MULTIPLIER	TEMPERATURE COEFFICIENT PPM °C	TEMP. SIGNIFICANT FIGURE	COEFF. MULTIPLIER	TOLERANCE* 10 PF OR LESS	TOLERANCE* OVER 10 PF	TOLERANCE*
BLACK	0	1	0	0.0	-1	±2.0 pF	±20%	±20%
BROWN	1	10	-33	1.0	-10	±0.1 pF	±1%	
RED	2	100	-75	1.5	-100		±2%	
ORANGE	3	1000	-150	2.2	-1000		±3%	+100%, -0%
YELLOW	4	10,000	-220	3.3	-10,000			±5%
GREEN	5		-330	4.7	+1	±0.5 pF	±5%	
BLUE	6		-470	7.5	+10			
VIOLET	7		-750		+100			
GRAY	8	.01	+150 To 1500		+1000	±0.25 pF		+80%, -20%
WHITE	9	.1	+100 To -750		+10,000	±1.0 pF	±10%	±10%
SILVER								
GOLD								

*Tolerance on Class 3 Ceramic Capacitors is indicated by its code, either ±20% (Code M) or +80, -20% (Code Z).

LETTER	TOLERANCE 10PF OR LESS	TOLERANCE OVER 10PF
B	±0.1 pF	±1%
C	±0.25 pF	±2%
D	±0.5 pF	±5%
F	±1.0 pF	±10%
G	±2.0 pF	±20%
J		
K		
M		

DISC CERAMICS (5-DOT SYSTEM)
1st Significant Figure, 2nd Significant Figure, Multiplier, Tolerance, Temperature Coefficient

DISC CERAMICS (3-DOT SYSTEM)
1st Significant Figure, 2nd Significant Figure, Multiplier

MOLDED-INSULATED AXIAL LEAD CERAMICS
1st Significant Figure, 2nd Significant Figure, Multiplier, Tolerance, Temperature Coefficient

MOLDED CERAMICS Using Standard Resistor Color Code
1st Significant Figure, 2nd Significant Figure, Multiplier, Tolerance, White Band Distinguishes Capacitor From Resistor

TYPOGRAPHICALLY MARKED CERAMICS
Axial Leads — Capacitance, Temperature Coefficient, Tolerance
Radial Leads — Capacitance, Type, Temperature Coefficient

BUTTON CERAMICS
1st Significant Figure, 2nd Significant Figure, Multiplier
Viewed From Soldered Surface

STANDOFF CERAMICS
1st Significant Figure, 2nd Significant Figure, Multiplier, Tolerance, Temperature Coefficient

HIGH-CAPACITANCE TUBULAR CERAMICS INSULATED OR NONINSULATED
1st Significant Figure, 2nd Significant Figure, Multiplier, Tolerance, Voltage (Optional)

TEMPERATURE COMPENSATING TUBULAR CERAMICS
1st Significant Figure, 2nd Significant Figure, Multiplier, Tolerance, Temperature Coefficient

EXTENDED RANGE T. C. TUBULAR CERAMICS
1st Significant Figure, 2nd Significant Figure, Temp. Coeff. Multiplier, Tolerance, Multiplier, T.C. Significant Figure

FEEDTHROUGH CERAMICS
1st Significant Figure, 2nd Significant Figure, Tolerance, Multiplier, Temperature Coefficient

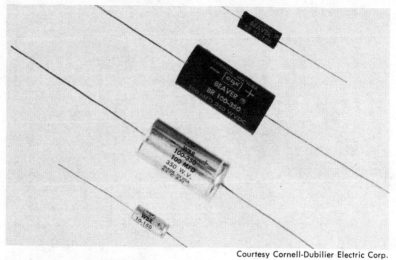

Courtesy Cornell-Dubilier Electric Corp.

(A) Tubular type.

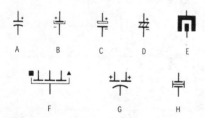

(B) Metal can type.

Courtesy Mallory Electric Co.

Fig. 3-7. Electrolytic capacitors.

Fig. 3-8. Electrolytic-capacitor symbols.

must go to the point with the most positive voltage, and the other side to the most negative potential, usually ground. Fig. 3-8 shows the symbols for designating electrolytics on schematics. The same symbol used for regular capacitors is sometimes employed. However, a plus sign (or plus and minus signs) is usually added to indicate the proper polarity as shown at A. The symbol at B removes any doubt that it is an electrolytic. Other electrolytic-capacitor symbols are shown at C, D, and E.

More than one electrolytic capacitor is often enclosed in the same container. The negative side of all units will be connected together, but separate terminals or leads will be provided for the positive side of each. For example, the capacitor in Fig. 3-7B has three sections, with the positive side of each connected to a separate terminal. These multisection capacitors are sometimes designated by the symbols A through F in Fig. 3-8—a separate symbol for each section. Occasionally the symbol at F, showing three sections, will be encountered.

The symbol at G is preferred by some manufacturers for a two-section capacitor. Notice the small rectangle and triangle near two sections in symbol F. In units enclosed in a metal can with the various sections are connected to terminals at the bottom (Fig. 3-7B), small marks, such as a rectangle, triangle, or semicircle, are placed near them. These marks are stamped on the side of the can along with the respective value and voltage rating of each section, and are also included alongside the symbol in the schematic. These marks may also be included alongside any of the other symbols. Thus, they serve to identify the separate sections.

Paper and other capacitors discussed previously will seldom have a value greater than 1 microfarad (it will usually be only a small fraction), whereas electrolytics will range from 1 microfarad up to 1 farad.

Because of their large values, electrolytics can store many more electrons. This makes them useful for smoothing out variations in voltage. They, therefore, find wide application as filter capacitors in power supplies. Here, the voltage may vary over wide limits, but will always have the same polarity. Hence, the fact that electrolytics must be connected correctly, polaritywise, is not a hindrance. Electrolytic capacitors are also widely used as coupling in audio circuits using transistors.

In certain applications, however, a large capacitor is needed for a circuit in which the voltage does change polarity. Special *nonpolarized* electrolytic units have been developed for this use. Symbol H shows one designation for such a capacitor.

VARIABLE CAPACITORS

Just as a variable resistor is useful in some circuits, variable capacitors are also needed. The most familiar example is

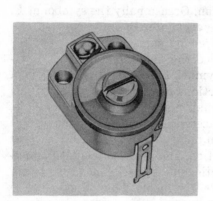

Courtesy Centralab, Electronics Div. of Globe-Union, Inc.

Fig. 3-9. Trimmer capacitors.

the tuning capacitor in many radios. As the tuning knob is rotated, the capacitor changes in value, causing its associated circuit to tune in the signal from the desired station.

Two other types of variable capacitors are shown in Fig. 3-9. Their capacitance is changed by turning the screwdriver adjustment. This so-called "trimmer" is usually designed by symbols A, B, C, or D in Fig. 3-10. The arrowheads in A, C, and D signify that the capacitance of the unit is variable. The symbol at B signifies a preset adjustment. That is, once set it is not normally adjusted except for alignment.

Another type of variable capacitor is illustrated in Fig. 3-11. Here, two sets of plates, each consisting of several flat pieces of metal connected together, mesh as the shaft is turned. Air is the dielectric, and if the shaft is rotated so the movable set of

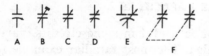

A   B   C   D   E
                    F

Fig. 3-10. Variable-capacitor symbols.

plates (called the *rotor*) is entirely surrounded by the stationary set (called the *stator*), the capacitance will be maximum. If rotated so the rotor extends out of the stator, it will be minimum. Miniature versions, often enclosed in plastic, are employed in transistor pocket radios.

The symbols for a trimmer capacitor may also be used for the unit just described, although the symbols shown at E and F in Fig. 3-10 are often employed. The arrow is used in various ways to designate a variable capacitance. For example, symbol E signifies a split rotor; that is, the stator plates are divided into two separate sections, but the rotor plates are not.

The capacitor pictured in Fig. 3-11 is actually two separate units connected together mechanically by a single shaft. The larger unit tunes one section of a radio, and the smaller unit another section. Rotating the shaft changes the capacitance of each unit simultaneously. This type is called a *ganged* capacitor and is usually designated by the symbol at F in Fig. 3-10. The dashed line between the arrows signifies that both sections are mechanically connected.

Fig. 3-11. A two-gang variable capacitor.

CODE LETTERS

Nearly all fixed and variable capacitors are designated by the code letter C. The letters M, E, or VC are sometimes employed to signify variable units.

QUESTIONS

1. What is the primary purpose of a capacitor?
2. Do electrons flow through a capacitor connected to an ac voltage?

3. What is the basic unit for measuring the electrical size of a capacitor?
4. What is the insulating material between the two sides of a capacitor called?
5. Are electrolytic capacitors generally suitable for ac circuits?
6. What is the most common use for electrolytic capacitors?
7. What does the prefix "micro" mean?
8. What is the movable portion of a tuning capacitor called?
9. What is the most common code letter for capacitors?
10. Identify the types of capacitors signified by the following symbols.

(A)   ⊣⊢   (B)   ⊣⊢   (C)   ⊣⊢

CHAPTER 4

Coils and Transformers

Just as any circuit or even a length of wire contains resistance and capacitance, it also will contain inductance—the electrical property of a coil.

WHAT IS A COIL?

A coil, or *inductor* as it is sometimes called, in its simplest form is just what its name implies—a wire wound into the shape of a coil. To be useful, however, coils must be wound in a certain way so that they will have the proper inductance value.

When current flows through a conductor, magnetic lines of force will be generated and will occupy the surrounding space. As long as the current is steady, the magnetic field will remain stationary, but if the current varies, the magnetic field will do likewise. Should the current stop suddenly (be shut off), the lines of force will collapse.

Whenever magnetic lines of force cross a conductor, an electric current is generated. Thus, the magnetic field produced by the current flowing in one turn of a coil will cut across other turns, setting up a current in them. This is repeated for each turn in the coil. The overall effect, when the current is made to increase, decrease, or change direction, is that the coil tends to oppose these changes. In other words, it tries to "smooth out" variations in current. A steady current (dc) will have no opposition except for the small resistance of the wire itself.

The electrical property of a coil is called *inductance*. The basic unit of measurement is the *henry* (abbreviated H), but like the farad, smaller units are often needed. The *millihenry* (mH), equal to one-thousandth of a henry, and the *microhenry* (μH), equal to one-millionth of a henry, are the more common units for specifying inductance values.

AIR-CORE COILS

The simplest coil has an air core and is constructed by winding a wire into a series of loops. The more usual method, however, is to wind the wire onto a plastic, paper, or other nonmetallic form. As long as this form is not capable of being magnetized (not a conductor of magnetic lines of force), the effect is the same as if no form were employed.

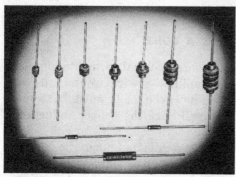

Fig. 4-1. Air-core coils.

Courtesy James Millen Mfg. Co., Inc.

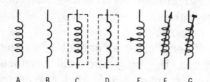

Fig. 4-2. Air-core coil symbols.

A   B   C   D   E   F   G

The air-core coils shown in Fig. 4-1 are wound on phenolic forms. The symbols used for air-core coils are given in Fig. 4-2. The loops may be shown open as in A or closed as depicted by the simpler symbol at B.

The coil may be molded in a plastic material so it resembles a resistor as shown in Fig. 4-3. The inset in this illustration shows the coil inside the molded unit. This type coil can also be shielded with a metal covering around it. In this case the symbols at C and D in Fig. 4-2, with the dashed line signifying the shield may be used.

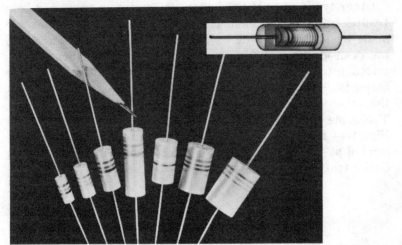

Courtesy J. W. Miller Div., Bell Industries

Fig. 4-3. Molded air-core coils.

Air-core coils may or may not be color coded with their value. In any case, the value is usually given either next to the symbol on the schematic or in the parts list, and will always be in the millihenry or microhenry range—never in henrys.

The code letter *L* is practically universal for coils of all types. However, the letters *RFC* (meaning Radio-Frequency Choke) may sometimes be used.

Adjustable Air-Core Coils

It is often desirable to change the inductance of a coil. This can be done by making the coil adjustable. Symbols for this type are shown at E, F, and G. It can also be represented by adding the adjustable symbol to the symbol at B. The symbol at E is often used to depict a coil having a slider that moves along the turns to "switch in" the desired portion. The symbol at F may be used to indicate a coil in which the inductance is changed by either compressing or expanding the turns to change the spacing between them. Both symbols are interchangeable, however.

POWDERED-IRON CORE COILS

Other types of coils have cores of ferrite or powdered iron (called iron-dust in some parts of the world). Ferrites are made by molding powdered iron or a similar substance into the desired shape. When such a core is brought near or inserted into a coil, it offers a more convenient path for the magnetic lines of force than does air. Hence, more lines cut the other conductors in the coil, increasing the inductance. The same methods used for the air-core type—A and B in Fig. 4-4—may also be used for powdered-iron core coils. The symbol at C is also popular. The core may be represented by either two or three dashed lines.

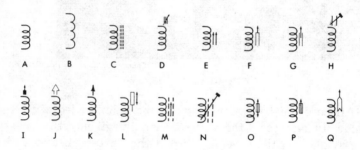

Fig. 4-4. Powdered-iron core coil symbols.

Adjustable Cores

To change the inductance of powdered-iron core coils, the core is usually moved in or out of the unit. This is called *permeability* tuning; an example of a coil tuned in this manner are shown in Fig. 4-5. Many types of symbols are used to indicate the adjustable core. Some are shown at D through Q in Fig. 4-4. Notice that most follow the same pattern of showing an arrow, but in a different manner.

Most permeability-tuned coils are in the millihenry range, but the value is seldom marked on the units. Nearly all manufacturers designate this type of coil by the letter *L*.

Fig. 4-5. Permeability-tuned coil.

Courtesy J. W. Miller Div., Bell Industries

IRON-CORE CHOKES

Another type of coil has a core of iron or steel and is usually referred to as a *choke,* since its function is to smooth out ("choke") variations in the current through it.

The construction of a typical iron-core choke is illustrated in Fig. 4-6. Instead of the core being a solid piece of metal, it is usually constructed from a series of thin sheets, or *laminations* (visible at the center of the figure). Insulated wire is wound in layers around the core, each layer being separated by additional insulation (usually paper). These layers may be left exposed, or the entire unit may be enclosed in a steel shell. Coils of this type are able to provide a large amount of inductance, usually in the henry range.

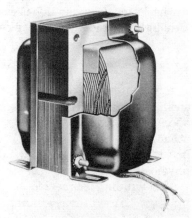

Fig. 4-6. Cutaway view of an iron-core choke.

Courtesy Merit Coil and Transformer Corp.

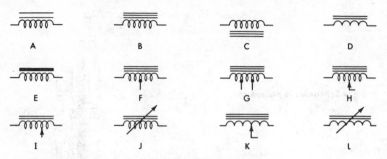

Fig. 4-7. Iron-core choke symbols.

The symbols for iron-core chokes are given at A, B, C, D, and E in Fig. 4-7. Note that they are the same as for other types of coils except that two or three solid lines are added to indicate the iron core. (The closed-loop symbol at D can be used for any of the core designations shown with open loops.) The symbols at F and G are for tapped units—that is, connections to different points on the winding permit particular portions or sections of the coil to be used.

Adjustable iron-core chokes are comparatively rare. Usually, instead of being continuously variable a series of taps and a switch are employed to make connection to the desired portion. When a continuously variable iron-core unit is used, however, it may be indicated by any one of the symbols at H, I, J, K, or L. These are the same as for a conventional choke, but with an arrow added to signify the inductance can be varied.

The letter L is usually used to indicate an iron-core choke, although occasionally FC (filter choke) is used.

TRANSFORMERS

A transformer is merely two or more coils positioned in such a manner that the magnetic field produced as a result of current flowing through one winding will cut across the other winding or windings. When this happens, a current will be *induced* in these other windings, even though they are not physically connected to the first.

The winding connected to the voltage source is called the *primary*. Any other winding is called a *secondary*. Besides causing a current flow in the secondary, the transformer can also change the amount of voltage. If the number of turns on both the primary and secondary are equal, then the voltage across each will be the same. With more turns on the secondary than on the primary, the secondary voltage will be higher. Conversely, if the secondary has fewer turns, its voltage will be lower.

Thus, the main function of a transformer is either to transfer an ac voltage from the primary to the secondary, or to step the voltage up or down. In either case the current in the secondary will vary exactly in step with the current in the primary. This phenomenon is used in *coupling,* or transferring, energy from one stage to another. Adding a capacitor across the winding will produce a combination that will accept a particular frequency and exclude all others. Current will flow in the secondary (which may also be *tuned* by a capacitor) at this particular frequency only.

Types of Transformers

Like coils, transformers may have either air, ferrite, or iron cores. Fig. 4-8 shows two air-core transformers. The one in Fig. 4-8A has a metal shield around it to remove any outside interference. Note also that this transformer has two capacitors mounted in the top of the metal "can" for tuning as explained previously. The transformer in Fig. 4-8B is unshielded.

 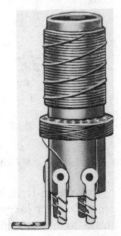

Courtesy J. W. Miller Div., Bell Industries

Fig. 4-8. Air-core transformers.

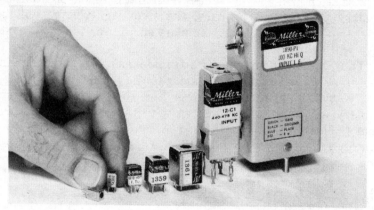

Fig. 4-9. Air-core transformer symbols.

Courtesy J. W. Miller Div., Bell Industries

Fig. 4-10. Powdered-iron core transformers.

The symbols for air-core transformers are given at A and B in
Fig. 4-9. Normally, air-core transformers are not variable,
since the only way this can be done is to move one of the coils
with respect to the other. If this is done, however, the symbols shown at C, D, and E are used.

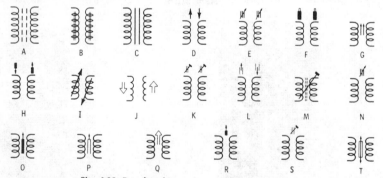

Fig. 4-11. Powdered-iron core transformer symbols.

Powdered-iron core transformers are available from very
small to very large units as shown in Fig. 4-10. While all these
units are enclosed in a metal can, others will not have this
covering. Capacitors for tuning may also be included within
the can. The symbols used to designate powdered-iron core

transformers are given in Fig. 4-11. Those at A, B, and C represent nonadjustable windings, Those at D through L usually represent transformers in which each winding is individually adjustable, while the symbols at M through T usually represent transformers in which one adjustment affects both windings. As for coils, there is a wide variation in the method used to depict the adjustment.

Iron-Core Transformers

There are many types of iron-core transformers. Fig. 4-12 shows three popular methods of construction. The unit in Fig. 4-12A is a low voltage transformer, while Fig. 4-12B illustrates a power transformer for a television receiver. In the latter unit all the windings are enclosed in a metal case with their leads brought out through an opening in the bottom. In Fig. 4-12C, the windings are enclosed in a solid epoxy case. This unit is used in transistor circuits.

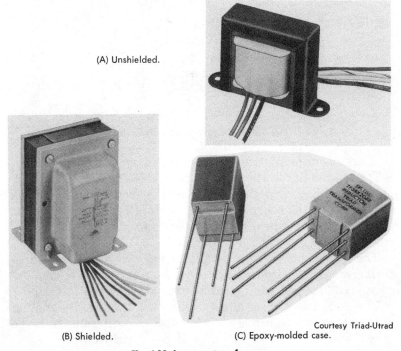

(A) Unshielded.

(B) Shielded.

(C) Epoxy-molded case.

Courtesy Triad-Utrad

Fig. 4-12. Iron-core transformers.

Iron-core transformer symbols are given in Fig. 4-13. Two or three lines may be used in the symbols at A, B, and C to indicate the iron core. Parts A, B, C, D, and E show five ways of indicating a unit having only two windings, while part F represents a transformer having four. Here, the primary is the winding on the left, and the top winding on the right is a low-voltage secondary (as signified by the fewer turns) for the filaments of the rectifier tube. The center winding is the high-voltage portion and is center tapped. The winding at the bottom is for the filaments of all other tubes in the receiver.

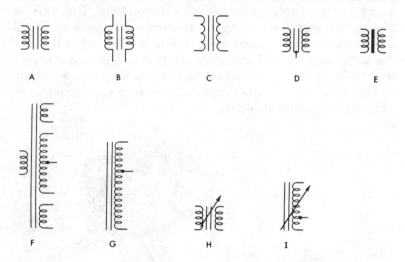

Fig. 4-13. Iron-core transformer symbols.

A special type of transformer, called an *autotransformer,* is symbolized at G. The portion from one end to the tap acts as one winding, and the complete coil, from one end to the other, acts as the other winding. Such units can step the voltage either up or down, and may have taps from which different voltages can be obtained.

The symbols at H and I indicate variable iron-core transformers. Like the iron-core chokes, these types are seldom encountered. Tapped windings are usually employed instead.

The code letter T is almost universal for the designation of iron-core transformers. The letter L will sometimes be used, however, to indicate air- and powdered-iron-core transformers.

QUESTIONS

1. What is the electrical property of a coil called?
2. What is the unit of measurement of the property in Question 1?
3. What effect does a coil have on steady dc flowing through it?
4. What enables one winding of a transformer to couple a current in another winding?
5. What is used to signify an iron core on a coil or transformer?
6. What is the more common name for an iron-core coil?
7. What is the name of the transformer winding in which the incoming current flows?
8. What do two or three rows of dashed lines between the windings of a transformer indicate?
9. What code letters are used to designate transformers?
10. Draw the symbol for an air-core coil.

CHAPTER 5

Electron Tubes

The entire foundation of electronics is based on the tiny, negatively charged particle called an *electron*. These electrons will flow from a negative to a positive voltage source if a complete conductive path is provided. This flow constitutes an electron current. Unless it can be controlled in some way, however, it will serve no useful purpose. Electron tubes are one type of device used to control this flow.

DIODE TUBES

Fig. 5-1 shows the elementary construction of the simplest of electron tubes—the *diode*. A length of special resistance wire, placed in the center of the unit, becomes hot when current flows through it. This heat causes electrons to be expelled from the surface of the wire (called the *filament*) into the surrounding vacuum. (The entire tube is evacuated of air, because the presence of oxygen would cause the filament to burn up.) Separated from the filament by the vacuum is another element, the *plate* (sometimes called the *anode*). If this plate is connected to a positive voltage source, the electrons "boiled off" the filament will flow toward it. If the voltage on this element is less positive than the filament, however, it will not attract electrons and no current will flow.

An alternating voltage (ac) placed on the plate will cause electrons to flow only during the time this element is more positive than the filament—not while it is more negative. Hence, we have the first control action of a tube—changing an ac voltage (on the plate) into a pulsating dc (on the filament). This action is called *rectification*. The pulsating dc is then smoothed out by an electrolytic capacitor.

The symbol for this type of tube is given at A in Fig. 5-2. The circle represents the glass or metal envelope, the pointed portion at the bottom of the circle is the filament, and the straight horizontal bar with the vertical line extending upward is the plate.

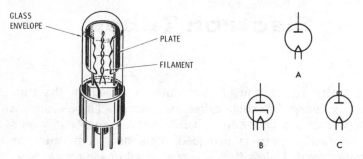

Fig. 5-1. Construction of a diode tube.   Fig. 5-2. Diode tube symbols.

Another type of diode tube is indicated by symbol B. Here, an additional element called the *cathode* is placed between the filament and plate. This element is a metal sleeve, coated with a special electron-emitting material. It fits over the filament, which now is used only to furnish heat. The advantage of this arrangement is that the heated cathode can produce more electrons than the filament and, in addition, its emission does not change with the alternating current often used to heat it. In this type of tube the filament is more properly called the *heater*.

TUBE BASES

Connections are made from the elements of the tube to pins in its base. The most popular bases for modern tubes are the 7- and 9-pin miniature, the 8-pin octal and the 12-pin compactron. In the 7-, 9-, and 12-pin types, the pins are merely symmetrically spaced wires which extend through the bottom of the glass envelope. A blank space between two of the pins serves as a guide for inserting the tube into the socket. In an octal-base tube, wires from the tube elements pass through the glass envelope and are soldered to pins embedded in a plastic or phenolic base. A keyed center post on the base serves to guide the tube into its socket.

There are many other base arrangements. Most will have a blank space, locating key, or other provision for orienting the tube in the socket. In some tubes, all pins are not connected to elements. In fact, some pins may even be omitted from the base if a locating key is employed.

Each pin is numbered for reference purposes. With the base pointed toward you, pin 1 is the first pin starting clockwise from the blank space or locating key. All other pins are numbered consecutively, reading clockwise around the base. (If a pin is omitted, the number ordinarily assigned to it is skipped, but the location of the other pins remains the same.)

These pin numbers are also placed on schematics next to the tube symbol, at the point where the respective tube elements enter the tube envelope. When this type of symbol is used, it is known as a *basing diagram*. By referring to the numbers beside the elements, you can locate the pin connected to each element.

In some tubes the connection to an element will be brought out the top to a cap instead of to a pin on the base. The cap is almost always connected to the plate. (In pre-World War II tubes it was often connected to another element called the grid.) A cap is usually symbolized by a small box around the lead, at the point where it enters the tube envelope. This is shown at *C* in Fig. 5-2, along with the pin numbers of the filaments.

TRIODE TUBES

The diode tube discussed previously performed only one control action—it converted ac to pulsating dc. The widest function of tubes, however, is to amplify a signal (i.e., make it greater). The diode tube cannot do this; in fact, it actually causes a slight reduction in signal strength. For amplification, at least one more element must be added between the cathode and plate, as shown by the drawing of a triode, or 3-element tube in Fig. 5-3. The added element, a cylinder made of fine-wire mesh, is called the *control grid*. This grid is represented

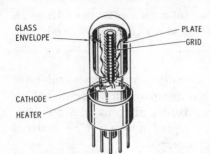

GLASS
ENVELOPE

PLATE

GRID

CATHODE

HEATER

Fig. 5-3. Construction of a triode tube.

by the dashed line between the cathode and plate in symbol A of Fig. 5-4.

In this type of tube, electrons will flow from cathode to plate, but they must first pass through the intervening control grid. Like the plate, the control grid is able to regulate the electron flow from the cathode—the more positive the control grid, the greater the electron flow, and vice versa. Being closer to the cathode, it exerts more influence than the plate on the electron flow.

TUBE VOLTAGES

The cathode—or in filament-type tubes, the minus side of the filament—is the reference point of all voltages in the tube since it emits the electrons. The cathode is connected either directly, or through a resistor, to this common reference point, generally referred to as simply *ground*. Hence the cathode voltage is either zero, or at most, slightly positive.

The grid is usually a few volts negative with respect to the cathode. Recall that a negative voltage will repel the electrons as they attempt to flow through the tube. However, electrons will still flow through the openings in the grid structure unless the voltage applied to it is too negative. Then, the grid repels all the electrons back to the cathode and the tube is said

Fig. 5-4. Triode tube symbols.

to be *cut off*. As the grid becomes less negative, however, more electrons will be drawn through it by the positive potential on the plate. If the grid becomes positive with respect to the cathode, it will also attract the electrons, and they will flow in the grid circuit.

As you can see, the electron flow of the plate will alternately increase and decrease if a varying voltage, such as an ac signal, is applied to the grid. These increases and decreases in the amount of electron flow through the plate resistor will cause much larger voltage variations at the plate than those of the grid signal which caused them.

SYMBOLS

The symbols used by most manufacturers to denote tubes are all very similar. Formerly, the zigzag line was used to represent the grid as shown at B in Fig. 5-4. The principal difference noted today will involve the weight and shape of the symbols denoting the various element inside the envelope. Notice the symbols at C and D in Fig. 5-4. Here the various elements are drawn slightly different, but they are easily recognizable. The elements inside the envelope may be tilted, drawn backwards, upside down, or in various other arrangements. The envelope may be drawn as a circle, as in A, B, and C of Fig. 5-4, or elongated, as in D and E. It may even be eliminated entirely. However, the basic symbol remains the same. In the remaining sections of this chapter, these variations will not be mentioned, but remember they will exist.

Another item is included with the symbols of Fig. 5-4. Notice the numbers near the point where the symbol for the individual elements enter the envelope. These numbers denote the pin number of the base to which this element is connected. Here again, the method of showing the pin numbers by various manufacturers will vary.

TETRODE TUBES

In Chapter 3 it was stated that a capacitive effect would exist between two conductors separated by an insulator. In the previously discussed triode tube, a certain amount of capacitance exists between the grid and plate. The *interelectrode ca-*

pacitance, as it is called, is detrimental to circuit operation in certain applications. To reduce its value, a fourth element, called a *screen grid,* can be placed between the grid and plate. Such a tube is called a *tetrode,* and its symbol is shown in Fig. 5-5. Notice the additional element, which looks exactly like the control grid in the drawing. In fact, its physical construction is very similar, but unlike the control grid, it is connected to a high positive voltage. A bypass capacitor, usually connected from the screen grid to common ground, makes this element appear at neutral (ground) to any signal voltage in the tube. As a result, the shielding action of the screen greatly reduces the effect of the capacitance between the control grid and plate. In addition, tetrode tubes are characterized by a much higher gain (provide more amplification) than can be obtained from a triode.

Fig. 5-5. Symbol for a tetrode tube.

PENTODE TUBES

The tetrode tube would seem to be ideal, since it overcomes the disadvantage of the interelectrode capacitance found in a triode, and at the same time gives more amplification. But its effectiveness is limited by another phenomenon known as *secondary emission.* As the electrons from the cathode strike the plate, some of them bounce off and some of the electrons already on the surface of the plate are also knocked loose. All these are attracted by the positive potential on the screen. Thus, the screen grid receives more than its share of electrons while the plate, which is the intended destination of the electrons, receives less. As a result, more electrons flow in the screen circuit (known as screen current) and fewer in the plate circuit (plate current).

The effect of secondary emission can be overcome by adding another element, similar in construction to the control and screen grids, between the screen and plate. This element is called the *suppressor* grid, and the type of tube in which it appears is called a *pentode.* The suppressor is connected to either the cathode or ground. Recall that a positive voltage is a point where there is a deficiency of electrons, and that a negative voltage is a point where there is an excess. The suppressor grid, having far more electrons than the plate, repels the secondary-emission electrons back to the plate before they have an opportunity to reach the screen grid.

The symbol for the pentode tube is shown at A in Fig. 5-6. Notice that it is the same as the symbol for the tetrode except for an additional grid between the plate and screen.

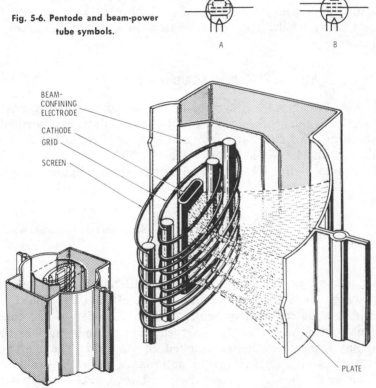

Fig. 5-6. Pentode and beam-power tube symbols.

A   B

Fig. 5-7. Construction of a beam-power tube.

BEAM-POWER TUBES

The *beam-power* tube is often thought of as being a pentode, although its operation is more like that of the tetrode. Instead of a suppressor grid, it has two metal vanes (called *beam-forming plates*) positioned in such a way as to guide or focus the electrons toward the plate (Fig. 5-7). In addition, the wires of the screen and control grids are in line, permitting more electrons to flow through. In this way, the tube can deliver much greater power.

The beam-forming plates are connected to the cathode inside the tube. The pentode (A in Fig. 5-6) symbol is used for the beam-power tube. However, sometimes the tetrode symbol (Fig. 5-5) or the symbol at B in Fig. 5-6 (which shows the beam-forming elements drawn differently) are also used. In either instance, a tube manual will have to be consulted to determine whether or not the tube in question is a beam-power type.

PENTAGRID TUBES

Fig. 5-8 shows the symbol for a *pentagrid* tube. It has a total of five grids between the cathode and plate, and normally performs two functions. For example, in a radio the first is that of the local oscillator, a stage which generates a high-frequency signal. The first grid acts as the oscillator grid and

Fig. 5-8. Symbol for a pentagrid tube.

the second as the plate. Electrons will flow on through it, however, toward the conventional plate of the tube. The third grid acts as the control grid for the remainder of the tube. This portion is similar to a conventional pentode and has the signal from the antenna applied to its grid. The electron stream is already varying in accordance with the oscillator frequency when it reaches the third grid. The two signals (from the oscillator and antenna) beat together, or *heterodyne,* producing a new signal which varies in the same manner as the signal applied to the third grid, but has a frequency equal to the difference between the two signals. This action is called *mixing.* The fourth grid (connected to the second) functions as the screen for the pentode section, and the fifth functions as the suppressor.

MULTIFUNCTION TUBES

Two or more tube functions are often combined in a single envelope. Some of the more popular combinations are: two diodes; two triodes; two diodes and a triode or pentode; and a triode and pentode. The elements for both tubes are sometimes drawn side by side in the symbol, as shown at A in Fig. 5-9.

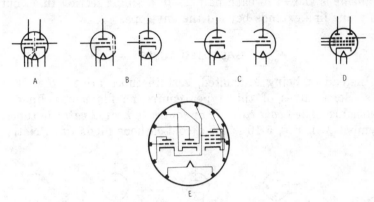

Fig. 5-9. Multifunction tube symbols.

The dashed line through the center represents a shield placed between the two sections to prevent interaction. Some tubes do not have this shield. If the two halves are in separate circuits they will usually be drawn as shown at B. Here, the dotted line at one side signifies that there is another section of the tube. Symbol C, with the dotted lines omitted and the side left open, will sometimes be used instead. You may occasionally find schematics in which one half of a dual-section tube will be completely enclosed within the circle, exactly like the single-section tube shown previously. The parts list will usually indicate that the tube is a multifunction type, or if not, a tube manual can be consulted.

Another type of multifunction tube is depicted by symbol D. Here the tube is actually a dual-pentode, except that the same cathode, control grid, and screen grid serve (are common to) both sections. In other tubes only the cathode may be shared. If so, and if each section is drawn at a different place on the schematic, the cathode will be shown in both places but the same pin number will be placed beside the cathode symbol.

In some multifunction tubes the filament is tapped in the center so that it can be operated from either 6 or 12 volts. Two filament connections will be shown in one half of the tube and one in the other half, as depicted by symbol B of Fig. 5-9. An untapped filament will be shown by symbol C. Here, one side of the filament connection is given in each section. The filament is shown in each half, as in a single-section tube, but only one line extends beyond the envelope.

GAS-FILLED TUBES

Instead of being evacuated, certain tubes are filled with a gas. Some tubes of this type require no filament voltage—hence are called *cold cathode* or *ionically heated cathode* tubes. Symbol A in Fig. 5-10 is for a cold-cathode diode tube. Notice

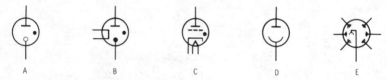

A   B   C   D   E

Fig. 5-10. Gas tube and phototube symbols.

that instead of a flat bar, a circle is used to represent the cathode, and no filament is shown. Sometimes this circle is replaced by a dot, as at B. In either symbol, a smaller dot, indicating a gas-filled tube, also appears inside the envelope. The other connection shown inside symbol B is a wire between two pins on the tube base. Its purpose is to open another circuit when the tube is removed. This protects the equipment if accidentally turned on with the tube out of the socket.

The symbol for another type of gas-filled tube, called a *thyratron,* is given at C. It is the same as the symbol for a triode except for the dot inside the envelope. The thyratron is used in certain control applications.

PHOTOTUBES

Symbol D in Fig. 5-10 depicts a different type of tube. Certain materials—potassium, sodium, and cesium, for example—give off small quantities of electrons when exposed to light. A curved piece of metal with a coating of this photo-sensitive material acts as the cathode. The plate (anode) is a metal rod in front of it. When light strikes the photosensitive material, electrons are released and flow to the plate. In the symbol, the curved portion represents the cathode, and the flat bar (or a dot or circle) represents the plate (usually called the anode in a phototube).

The symbol for another type of phototube, called a *photomultiplier*, is shown at E in Fig. 5-10. The main cathode is the curved element at the center from which electrons flow to the first element at the bottom left of the symbol. This element, in turn, emits more electrons to the next similar element. (Notice that the symbol for the elements around the outside of the tube are a combination of the photocathode and anode symbols.) These elements attract the electrons, and each in turn emits more electrons than the preceding one, until finally the element to the right of the cathode lead is reached. Here, the conventional anode symbol is used for the element from which the output is taken. Because of this multiplier action, many more electrons flow from the output than could flow from the tube at D.

CATHODE-RAY TUBES

Cathode-ray tubes are usually classified according to whether they employ electrostatic or electromagnetic deflection. The principal use for the former is in oscilloscopes, while the television picture tube is the most familiar application for the latter.

Electrostatic Deflection

Fig. 5-11 shows the construction of a typical electrostatic tube. The electrons leave the heated cathode, as in other tubes, and are attracted by the positive voltage on the accelerating anode. First, however, they must flow through the control grid, a metal cylinder with a hole in one end. A negative voltage on this element controls the number of electrons allowed to pass through. From the control grid, the electrons pass on to the focus anode, which concentrates them into a narrow beam. After the electrons leave the focusing anode, their velocity is increased by two high-voltage accelerating anodes.

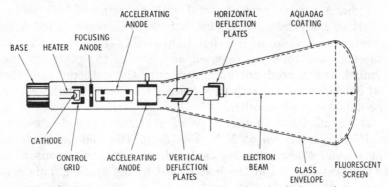

Fig. 5-11. Construction of an electrostatically deflected cathode-ray tube.

The remaining electrodes are the deflection plates. The two horizontal plates move the beam from side to side, and the vertical-deflection plates move it up and down. After passing through and being influenced by the deflection plates, the beam strikes the screen with great force, causing a fluorescent coating on the screen to glow. The brightness depends on the number of electrons and their velocity.

Symbol A in Fig. 5-12 is sometimes used to depict an electrostatic cathode-ray tube. (Note its similarity to the tube.) The elements are shown in the order in which they appear in the tube—from left to right they are the heater, cathode, control grid, focusing electrode, and accelerating anodes. The two sets of deflection plates are depicted by the pointed elements that are next in line.

At other times the symbol for the electrostatic cathode-ray tube resembles that of a conventional tube, as shown at B. Notice that here the focus electrode is placed between two sections of the accelerating anode. Where other arrangements are used, the schematic symbol shows the actual arrangement of the elements.

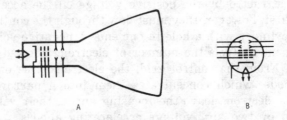

Fig. 5-12. Electrostatically deflected cathode-ray tube symbols.

Electromagnetically Deflected Cathode-Ray Tubes

The most familiar type of electromagnetically deflected cathode-ray tube is the one in your television set. It is similar to the electrostatic tube, except it has no deflection plates. Instead, the beam is deflected both horizontally and vertically by coils around the neck of the tube. Often there are no focusing electrodes either; the electron beam is converged on the screen by a permanent magnet or an electromagnet around the neck.

Electromagnetically deflected cathode-ray tubes employ either 8-, 12-, or 14-pin bases. The symbol at A in Fig. 5-13 is for a tube having electrostatic focus. Note how it resembles the actual tube. The elements are arranged in the order

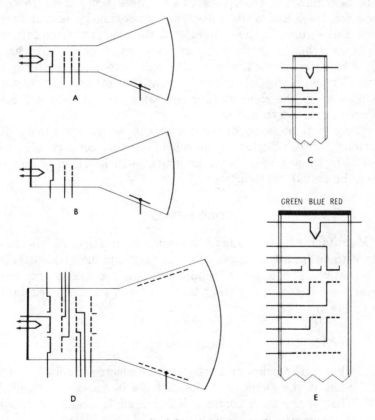

Fig. 5-13. Magnetically deflected cathode-ray tube symbols.

they appear in the tube. In this case they are the heater, cathode, control grid, first anode (screen), and focus electrode. The connection to the line inside the envelope at the lower right is the second anode or high voltage connection. This connection is made to a contact on the side of the tube instead of through the base. The symbol at B is the same, except here the focus electrode is omitted, signifying it is for a tube with external focus. The symbol at C shows still another way of representing the tube. This symbol represents the tube neck and the elements are drawn as shown. In this case the high-voltage connection is not shown, but a note on the schematic will show where the connection is made.

The symbols at D and E in Fig. 5-13 shows two methods of representing color-tv picture tubes. These are similar to the ones for black-and-white tubes shown previously, except they have three guns. In the symbol at D the elements from left to right are: heater, cathodes, control grids, screen grids, and focus electrode. Note the focus electrode is common to all three guns. The high-voltage connection is at the bottom right. In the symbol at E, the elements are the same, except they are arranged from top to bottom.

There will be some difference in the internal make-up of various black-and-white (monochrome) and color-tv picture tubes. In these cases, the arrangement will be changed to reflect the actual construction.

CODE LETTERS

Manufacturers are almost unanimous in selecting the letter V to designate all types of tubes (vacuum or gas) on their schematics. The letter T is also employed occasionally; but most save it for designating transformers, as discussed in a previous chapter.

QUESTIONS

1. What is the primary purpose of all electron tubes?
2. What is the purpose of the cathode in an electron tube?
3. What is the most common letter used to designate tubes on schematics?
4. What is a cold-cathode tube?

5. What is the most common type of cathode-ray tube?
6. From what element of the tube is the output normally taken?
7. How are connections made to the various elements inside the tube?
8. Draw the symbol for a triode tube.
9. Draw a thyratron tube.
10. Draw a dual-section tube; one section a pentode, and the other a triode.

CHAPTER 6

Semiconductors

The primary purpose of *semiconductors,* or *solid-state* devices as they are sometimes called, is to control the flow of electrons. They can be employed in almost any application that a tube can, and in some where a tube cannot.

WHAT IS A SEMICONDUCTOR?

The term "semiconductor" refers to a group of materials with a resistance between that of insulators and conductors. A comprehensive study of semiconductor theory is beyond the scope of this book. However, the following brief explanation will aid in understanding this chapter.

The resistance of a material is largely determined by the number of electrons in the outer shell of an atom of the material. Insulators have from five to eight electrons in this outer shell while conductors have three or less. Semiconductors have four electrons in the outer shell—silicon, germanium, and selenium are three of the most common materials.

The pure semiconductor material must be treated—called doping—before it is useful. Certain impurities are introduced into the pure semiconductor material to produce the necessary characteristics. By adding a small quantity of material having five electrons in its outer shell an excess electron will result in the material produced. This excess electron can be caused to move about in the semiconductor crystal. Since the electron has a negative charge, the semiconductor material treated in this manner is said to be *n-type material*.

If a material having only three electrons in its outer shell is combined with the semiconductor material, a deficit of electrons will exist in the material. In other words, there will be "holes" at some points in the bond between the atoms where electrons would normally exist. Since material doped in this manner lacks the number of electrons to form a perfect bond in the resulting crystal, the material is said to be *positive* or *p-type* material.

Keep in mind, the overall number of electrons and protons in the resulting crystal has not been changed. That is, the material is electrically neutral. It has just been given the capacity to transfer an electric current, When a battery is connected to the two sides of a piece of n-type material, the excess electrons are attracted to the positive terminals of the battery and the electrons from the negative terminal of the battery move into the material to fill any holes that exist in the material. Thus, electrons are the current carriers in n-type material.

If this same battery is connected to p-type material, which has a deficiency of electrons, conduction is often thought of as being a movement of holes toward the negative terminal of the battery. However, just as holes move from the positive to the negative side of the material, electrons from the battery also move from the negative to the positive side. Since the p-type crystal has a deficiency of electrons, holes are considered the current carriers in the material.

THE PN JUNCTION

For most applications a means must be obtained to control the flow of electrons (or holes) and to allow conduction in only one direction. This cannot be accomplished with either the p- or n-type material by itself. However, by placing a chip of n-type material directly adjacent to a piece of p-type material, the conditions are met to allow conduction in one direction but not in the other. Fig. 6-1 shows how this is accomplished. When the two materials are brought together (Fig. 6-1A), the excess electrons in the n-type material immediately adjacent to the p-type material will tend to move over into the p-type material and combine with the holes in the p-type material to maintain equilibrium. However, this combining occurs only in a very thin layer of the material. This is the pn junction and is the basis for most semiconductor devices. Many ways are employed to produce the two adjacent materials and form the junction, but the result is the same.

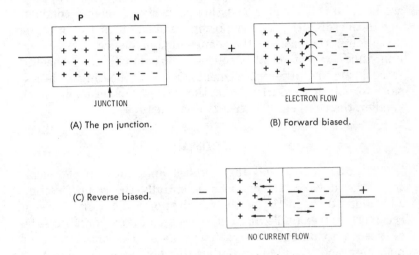

(A) The pn junction.

(B) Forward biased.

(C) Reverse biased.

Fig. 6-1. Operation of the pn junction.

Now let's see what happens when a battery is connected to the two layers of material. If the battery is attached so the positive terminal is connected to the p-type material and the negative terminal to the n-type material as shown in Fig. 6-1B, the excess of electrons from the negative terminal of the battery flow into the n-type material and rush toward the junction. Likewise, it can be said that the holes in the p-type material rush toward the same junction. Here the electrons and the holes combine with one another and current flow—electrons from minus to plus and holes from plus to minus—occurs through the device. This is said to be forward biased, since the voltage (bias) conditions are proper for current to flow.

If the battery connections are reversed (Fig. 6-1C), the holes move toward the positive terminal of the battery and the electrons move toward the negative terminal. Therefore, with both holes and electrons moving away from the junction, little or no current flow occurs through it. There is no combining of holes and electrons at the junction. This is said to be the reverse-bias condition.

Now we have the conduction properties needed to produce what has been termed a *semiconductor*. Semiconductor devices act as conductors in one direction and insulators in the opposite direction. To be sure, there are exceptions as we will see later in this chapter, but this property of readily conducting in one direction and opposing conduction in the opposite direction is the basis of the semiconductor device. Unlike vacuum tubes, the material is solid—no vacuum or gas is needed to separate the different elements. Also, no heating is necessary to obtain conduction and the device can be made much smaller than is possible with a vacuum tube.

RECTIFIERS

The power rectifier is the simplest and oldest of the semiconductor devices. It performs essentially the same function as a diode tube. In the power supplies of radio and television receivers, for example, it converts the ac line voltage into the dc needed to operate the various stages. The oldest type of metallic rectifier used in entertainment-type equipment is made of selenium. Fig. 6-2 shows some of the many types available. Some of these units actually contain four separate power rectifiers connected together.

Silicon rectifiers (Fig. 6-3) are also very popular. Most of the units pictured in Figs. 6-1 and 6-2 can be soldered directly into the circuit; others may be plugged into a holder.

The symbol adopted for power rectifiers is given at A in Fig. 6-4. In some instances, part of the symbol will not be shaded, as shown at B and C, or the entire symbol may be left unshaded, as shown at D. Often the symbol is enclosed in a circle, which represents the cue, as shown at E.

The bar portion in the symbol corresponds to the cathode of a vacuum tube. That is, electrons flow from it toward the arrowhead. This bar portion of the symbol will sometimes be labeled with a "+" sign or the letters CATH. The same markings may be stamped on the unit itself. Notice, in Fig. 6-3, the symbol is stamped on the unit to show the polarity.

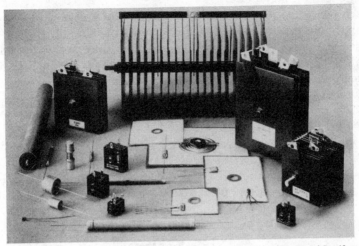

Courtesy International Rectifier

Fig. 6-2. Typical selenium rectifiers.

Letter Codes

There is much disagreement among manufacturers about which letters to use in designating power rectifiers. Consequently, while CR and D are the most common, the letters *SE*, *X, Y, E*, and *REC*, among others, may be encountered.

SIGNAL DIODES

Like power rectifiers, signal or crystal diodes perform the same function as a diode tube. The difference between the power rectifier and the signal diode, however, is in the function

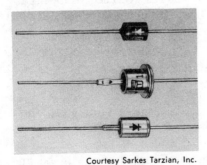

Courtesy Sarkes Tarzian, Inc.

Fig. 6-3. Typical silicon rectifiers.

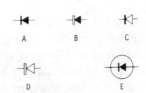

Fig. 6-4. Rectifier symbols.

each performs in a circuit. Power rectifiers are used in power-supply circuits to handle large amounts of current. Signal diodes are used in signal circuits and thus they pass only small values of current. Typical signal diodes are shown in Fig. 6-5. Some have leads that are soldered into the circuits; others are plugged into a holder.

The symbols for signal diodes are the same as those shown in Fig. 6-4 for power rectifiers. Like power rectifiers, a "+" sign or the letters CATH are often placed near the bar portion of the symbols. Either marking may also appear on the end of the unit itself, although a colored dot or ring or some other identification is often placed there instead.

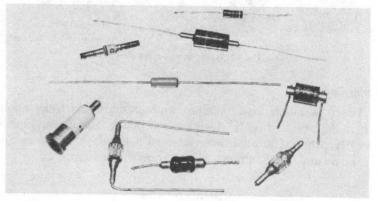

Fig. 6-5. Signal diodes.

Letter Codes

Like the power rectifier, many letters are used to designate signal diodes. While CR and D are the most common, *E, SC, XD, X,* and *Y* are also used.

TRANSISTORS

In 1948, Drs. William Shockley, John Bordeen, and Walter H. Brattain of Bell Telephone Laboratories announced their development of the first transistor. Since that time, the transistor has revolutionized the electronics industry. It can be used in practically every application that a tube can be and in some it can't.

The principal advantages of the transistor over a tube are: (1) it is much smaller; hence, equipment can be made much more compact; (2) its power requirements are much lower, so large power supplies are not needed; in fact, a small flashlight cell will operate a transistor for a long time; (3) it has no heater; this further simplifies the power supply and reduces ventilation problems; and (4) it has a longer life expectancy and is less fragile.

The word "transistor" is a broad term applied to the entire field of those semiconductor devices which have three or more terminals. There are many sizes and shapes of transistors. Each has its own particular application where it performs the same function as a vacuum tube—amplifying, mixing, oscillating, and switching, to name a few.

Transistor Construction

In function, the transistor corresponds roughly to the triode vacuum tube. Fig. 6-6 shows the elementary construction of a

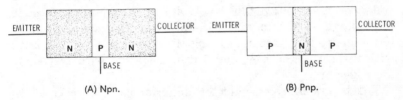

(A) Npn.   (B) Pnp.

Fig. 6-6. Elementary transistor.

transistor. Notice it contains two of the pn junctions described previously. Just as adding the grid to the vacuum tube made it possible to control a large voltage with a small voltage on the grid, adding the third layer to our semiconductor "sandwich" makes it possible to control a large current with a much smaller current. Transistors are considered to be current-operated devices, while tubes are voltage-operated devices, but the result is the same—a small quantity controlling a much larger quantity.

In Fig. 6-6A two layers of n-type semiconductor material are separated by a thin layer of p-type material. Connections are made to each of the layers as shown. If a negative voltage is connected to the n-type material labeled emitter and a slightly positive voltage is connected to the p-type base material, the junction between the two will be forward biased as explained previously. Thus current will flow between the two points. The base region is very thin and electrons will pass through it easily. Thus, when the proper voltages are connected to the base and emitter to forward bias the junction, a much larger current can flow between the emitter and the collector, which is connected to a more positive voltage. If the current between the emitter and the collector is varied, the current between the emitter and the collector will vary in step. The elementary transistor in Fig. 6-6A has two layers of n-type material separated by a layer of p-type material. Thus, it is called an npn transistor. In an npn transistor, the base is made negative with respect to the collector and the emitter is made negative with respect to the base. Keep in mind the actual voltages are not important; they can be negative, positive, or even zero on a given element. What is important is the relationship of the voltage on a given element to the voltage on the other elements. For example, if the actual voltage on the collector is +6 volts and the voltage on the base is +2 volts, the base voltage will be 4-volts *negative* with respect to the voltage on the collector. Likewise, in this same example, if the emitter voltage is +1 volt, it will be a 1-volt negative with respect to the base and 5-volts negative with respect to the collector.

The layers of semiconductor material can be reversed as shown in Fig. 6-6B. Here the emitter and the collector are p-type material and the base is n-type material. Thus, it is termed a pnp transistor. Operation of this transistor is essentially the same as for the npn transistor, except all the voltages are reversed. That is, the emitter is the most positive element, the base is negative with respect to the emitter, and the collector is negative with respect to the base.

Fig. 6-7 shows the internal construction of one type of transistor. The semiconductor material is in the center. Connections from the various elements are then made to the leads extending up through the bottom of the case.

Transistor Symbols

The symbols for an npn transistor are given in Fig. 6-8. Notice that the arrowhead may be located at the point where the diagonal intersects the circle, as in A, or placed along the

Fig. 6-7. Internal view of a transistor.

Courtesy General Electric Co.

line as in B. The element with the arrowhead denotes the emitter, and the bar portion of the symbol, the base. The remaining element is the collector. The letters *E, B,* and *C* identify the elements. The emitter is shown at the top of symbol C. Even when the different elements are repositioned, the emitter is always the element with the arrowhead. The symbols at D and E are seldom encountered.

Fig. 6-9 shows the symbols for a pnp transistor. The only difference is in the direction of the arrowhead. In the npn transistor symbol it points *away* from the base, while for a pnp it points *toward* the base. In other words, it will always point in the direction *opposite* the flow of electrons.

FIELD-EFFECT TRANSISTORS

The transistors discussed previously are more properly called *bipolar transistors.* As stated previously they are essentially current-operated devices. The field-effect transistor is a

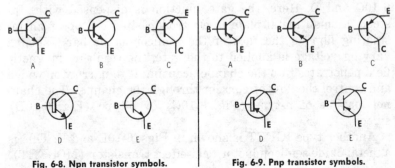

Fig. 6-8. Npn transistor symbols.

Fig. 6-9. Pnp transistor symbols.

87

voltage-operated device—more like that of the conventional vacuum tube. There are two basic types of field-effect transistors (abbreviated FET). The first is the junction field-effect transistor (JFET) and the second is the insulated-gate field-effect transistor (IGFET). Fig. 6-10A shows the elementary construction of the JFET. Here, connections are made to the two ends of a bar of n-type silicon. On the opposite face of the bar, a controlled amount of dopant has been added to create the two parallel facing strips of p-type material. Thus a pn junction is formed between each strip and the bar of n-type silicon. This is where the device gets the name *junction* FET. These two strips are connected together and are called the *gate* of the device. The connection to one end of the bar is called the *source,* and the connection to the other end is called the *drain.* Roughly, the source corresponds to the cathode of a vacuum tube, the gate the grid, and the drain the plate. The path through the bar from the source to the drain is called the *channel.* Nearly all the voltage across the JFET will pass through this channel with relatively little resistance. However, when voltage is applied to the gate, a small electrical field is built up around the gate which restricts the available channel width for current flow. As the gate voltage is increased still further, a point is reached where the channel is constricted across the full width and current is at a minimum. This is called *pinch-off.* Thus, as the voltage applied to the gate electrode is varied, the larger voltage from the source to the plate is caused to vary in step and we have amplification.

The channel can be made of n-type material as in Fig. 6-10A or of p-type material as shown in Fig. 6-10B. The former is sometimes called an NFET and the latter a PFET.

The elementary construction of an IGFET is shown in Fig. 6-10C and D. Here, the gate junction is dispensed with. Instead, a small metal plate is electrodeposited on top of an insulating film on the face of the semiconductor bar. When a varying voltage is applied to the gate, the resulting magnetic field penetrates into the channel, causing it to narrow or widen and control the flow of current through the channel. The channel may be of n-type (Fig. 6-10C) or p-type (Fig. 6-10D) silicon.

Another type IGFET is shown in Figs. 6-10E and F. This is a metal oxide semiconductor field-effect transistor (MOSFET).

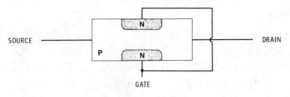

(A) N-channel JFET.

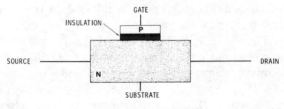

(B) P-channel JFET.

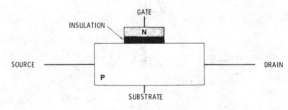

(C) N-channel IGFET.

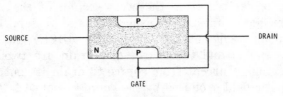

(D) P-channel IGFET.

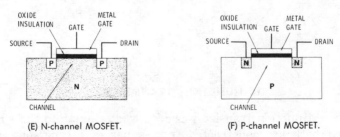

(E) N-channel MOSFET.

(F) P-channel MOSFET.

Fig. 6-10. Construction of FETs.

89

Its name is derived from the cross section of the wafer—a metal-film gate, an oxide insulation, and a semiconductor wafer. In an n-channel MOSFET (Fig. 6-10E), the channel is n-type silicon and the source and drain are two diffused p-type regions. Current from source to drain is controlled by the magnetic field produced by the voltage applied to the gate. MOSFETs may have either a single gate or dual gates.

FET Symbols

The symbols at A and B in Fig. 6-11 are for junction-type FETs. The symbol at A is for the n-channel and the one at B is for the p-channel FET. The symbols at C and D are for n-channel and p-channel IGFETs, respectively. Other arrangements are also produced. The symbol at E is for an IGFET with two gates. Many of the differences in IGFETs involve the bulk of the semiconductor material (called the substrate). Connections to it may be internal, external, or omitted (as at C and D). The symbols at F through I show some of the variations for n-channel units. The arrowhead would be reversed for p-type units. The symbols at J and K show a different way to draw the JFET symbol. The abbreviations in Fig. 6-11 are as follows: G, gate; D, drain; S, source; and U, substrate.

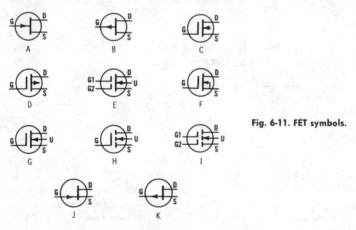

Fig. 6-11. FET symbols.

UNIJUNCTION TRANSISTORS

The unijunction transistor is somewhat similar to the FET in that both are constructed from a bar of n-type semiconductor material. As shown in Fig. 6-12, connections are made to each end of the bar for the two bases. Then a single pn junction is formed approximately one-quarter of the way down from the top end. Connections are made to the two bases and to the spot of p material which is the emitter. In operation, the UJT does not conduct until a certain voltage point is reached across two of the terminals, then it suddenly turns on. The symbol for a unijunction transistor with n-type base is given at A in Fig. 6-13, while the symbol at B is for a unit with p-type base.

As with tube symbols, the circle denoting the protective covering is sometimes omitted, but this is not recommended.

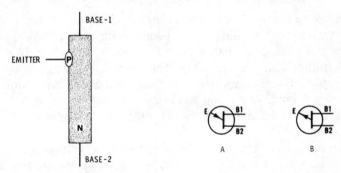

Fig. 6-12. UJT construction.

Fig. 6-13. UJT symbols.

Code Letters

Fewer letters are used to denote transistors of the various manufacturers than for other members of the semiconductor family. Q is the most popular. Nevertheless, the letters X, V, T, and TR are also employed.

OTHER SEMICONDUCTORS

There are many other types of semiconductors in use today. Some are not presently being used in consumer equipment, but no doubt you will encounter several of them as you examine various circuits. Only the more common will be discussed here.

Zener Diode

The zener diode (Fig. 6-14) is much like the power or signal diodes discussed previously. Its characteristics are very

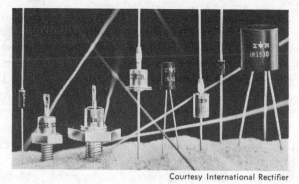

Courtesy International Rectifier

Fig. 6-14. Typical zener diodes.

similar to those of power or signal diodes. Recall that a diode allows current to flow in only one direction. In the reverse direction, the diode has a high resistance. However, if a voltage higher than that at which the diode is designed to operate is applied in this direction, the diode will break down and current will flow. A normal diode may be damaged under these conditions; the zener diode is designed to operate in this manner.

In operation, the zener diode serves as a voltage regulator; that is, when the voltage exceeds a given amount, the zener diode conducts, limiting the voltage to the desired value. Fig. 6-15 shows the symbols used to denote a zener diode. Those at A and C are probably the most popular. Any of the symbols can have the circle as at A, B, E, F, and G or without as at C and D. The zener diode is also known as a backward diode, breakdown diode, avalanche diode, and voltage-regulator diode.

Thyristors

The term "Thyristor" is applied to a class of semiconductor devices that provide an on-off or triggered operation similar

Fig. 6-15. Zener diode symbols.

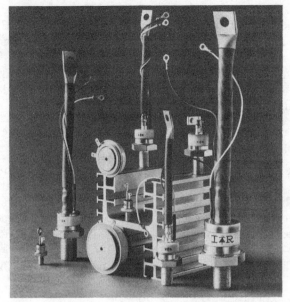

Courtesy International Rectifier

Fig. 6-16. Typical silicon-controlled rectifiers.

to that of a thyratron. The most common of these devices is the silicon controlled rectifier of Fig. 6-16. They are represented by the symbols at A and B in Fig. 6-17. These devices will not conduct until a "trigger" current is applied to the gate terminal. Then they will conduct very readily. The sym-

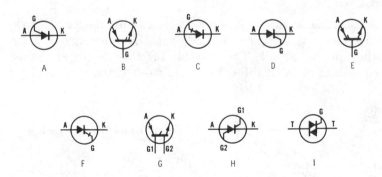

Fig. 6-17. Thyristor symbols.

bol at C is for a gate turn off type. Here the gate current turns the unit off instead of on. The symbols at A, B, and C are for units with n-type gates. The ones at C, D, and E are for the same units, except they have p-type gates. Tetrode-types are also available. The symbols at G and H are for a reverse-blocking tetrode-type semiconductor controlled switch. The symbol for a bidirectional triode thyristor, also called a triac or gated switch is given at I in Fig. 6-17.

Tunnel Diode

In the normal semiconductor, it takes a certain amount of time for the current carriers to move through the unit. In the tunnel diode, however, they appear to move at the speed of light—according to Einstein's theory, the ultimate speed in the universe. At the same time, a tunnel diode is capable of am-plifying—a function not normally obtained in a two-element device. Explanation of the tunnel diode is beyond the scope

Fig. 6-18. Tunnel diode symbols.

of this book. Tunnel diodes can be used in many types of cir-cuits where usually only a transistor or tube can be used. Temperature extremes and nuclear radiation have little effect on them. Fig. 6-18 shows the most common symbols used to depict a tunnel diode on schematics. As with other semi-conductor symbols, the circle may or may not be used.

Capacitive Diode

Also called a varactor, *Varicap,* reactance diode, or para-metric diode, the capacitive diode actually functions as a ca-pacitor in the circuit. The symbols for this device are given here instead of in Chapter 3 because most of the symbols used

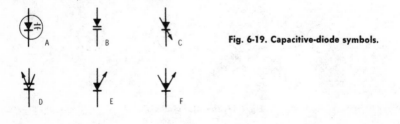

Fig. 6-19. Capacitive-diode symbols.

to depict it (Fig. 6-19) resemble those for the semiconductor diode. Recall that a semiconductor diode consists of a layer of p- and a layer of n-type material. When these two materials are joined, a layer forms at the junction which serves as an insulator. This condition is the same as for a capacitor— two conductors separated by an insulator. In the normal diode, steps are taken to minimize this capacitance. In the capacitive diode the capacitance is emphasized. The capacitance of a capacitive diode will vary, depending on the voltage across the diode. Thus, by varying the voltage, the capacitance varies, and a circuit can be "tuned." For example, by using a potentiometer to vary the voltage applied to the diode, they can be used to tune a tv receiver to the proper channel.

Photodiodes

The semiconductor diode is a very versatile device. There seems to be no end to the uses to which it can be put by simply varying the construction and composition. Silicon diodes are also sensitive to light. In some applications they function as a resistor whose value varies according to the amount of light striking it. In this use, they are usually called light-dependent resistors. Symbols for light-dependent resistors were given in Fig. 2-13.

In addition, a voltage can be generated when light strikes the diode. In this application it is called a solar cell. Fig. 6-20

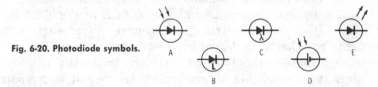

Fig. 6-20. Photodiode symbols.

shows symbols used to depict the solar cell. The symbols at A, B, and C resemble the diode symbol with the arrows, letter L, or Greek *lambda* (λ) signifying that it is light-sensitive. The symbol at D more nearly represents a battery (to be discussed in a later chapter). As with other diode symbols, the circle enclosing the symbol may or may not be employed, but it is recommended. Some diodes emit light when a voltage is impressed across them. The symbol at E in Fig. 6-20 is for a photoemissive-type diode. Note it is the same as the symbol at A, except for the direction of the arrows.

Courtesy ITT Semiconductors

Fig. 6-21. Typical integrated circuits.

INTEGRATED CIRCUITS

The semiconductor components discussed up to this point have been what are termed "discrete components." That is, each was a separate, distinct item. It has been mentioned that semiconductors can be made very small. In fact, several—even hundreds—transistors, diodes, resistors, etc., can be fabricated on a single tiny semiconductor chip. Integrated circuits (Fig. 6-21) can be produced to fulfill practically any application desired. In fact, without integrated circuits, it is doubtful if modern calculators, computers, etc., could be produced. Certainly, the small compact units of today would not be possible.

The integrated component is normally represented on schematics, by the triangular symbol of A or B in Fig. 6-22. Sometimes, instead of the triangle, a square or rectangle will be used, but the triangle, which represents an amplifier is far more common. The internal circuitry is usually not shown. Since it is impossible to "see" inside the circuit and repair it, the internal circuitry is not of interest. Also, some of the circuitry is considerably different than what would be employed if conventional discrete components were used. Therefore, just the triangular symbol, with leads extending from it to show

Fig. 6-22. Integrated circuit symbols.

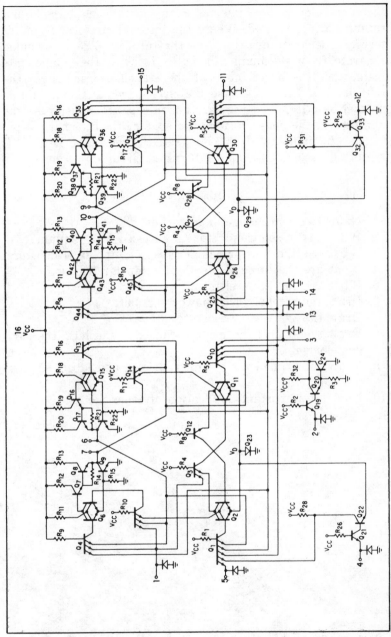

Courtesy ITT Semiconductors

Fig. 6-23. Internal circuitry of an integrated circuit.

the connection of any external components, such as coils and tuning devices is used. Where the internal circuitry is of interest, a separate drawing like that of Fig. 6-23 is included separate from the main schematic, to show the components inside the IC. Notice, none of the transistors shown in the schematic of Fig. 6-23 have the circles around them. This is normal practice, since they are not in separate envelopes. The numbers at the points around the edge of the schematic refer to the pin numbers of the integrated circuit. The letters IC are often used to designate integrated circuits on schematics.

QUESTIONS

1. Name two semiconductor materials.
2. Why must a semiconductor be enclosed in a vacuum?
3. What are the two principal types of bipolar transistors.
4. What are the three elements of a bipolar transistor?
5. What are the three elements of a FET.
6. Draw the symbol for a power rectifier.
7. Draw the symbol for a crystal diode.
8. Draw the symbol for an npn transistor and label the various elements.
9. Draw the symbol for a pnp transistor and label the various elements.
10. Name an important application of zener diodes.

CHAPTER 7

Switches and Relays

When a circuit is closed, a complete path is provided over which electrons can flow. Conversely, when open no path exists and hence the circuit is inoperative. Some means must be provided to open or close many of the circuits in electronic equipment. Each of the devices discussed in this chapter will perform this switching function.

SPST SWITCHES

The simplest switch is the knife switch illustrated in Fig. 7-1. When the arm moves down, it engages the clips at the end and completes the circuit to which it is connected. Such a device is called a *single-pole, single-throw* switch (abbreviated spst). It can make connections for only one line, and at only one point. The symbols for spst switches are given in Fig. 7-2. All look alike except D and E, differing only in the arrowheads (which indicate the movable contact) and the small circles (which indicate the connection points).

Other types of construction can be used for the spst switch, such as the familiar on-off switch for controlling our house lighting. The toggle switch, slide switch, and radio or tv on-off switch (which is activated by rotating or pulling and pushing a shaft), are all spst units and are identified by the symbols in Fig. 7-2.

Fig. 7-1. A single-pole, single-throw knife switch.

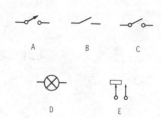

Fig. 7-2. Single-pole, single-throw switch symbols.

SPDT SWITCHES

The knife switch shown in Fig. 7-3 can be used to connect the center terminal to either outside terminal. It still makes connections for only one line at a time, but to either point. Called a *single-pole, double-throw* (abbreviated spdt) switch, it appears in many forms—toggle, slide, rotary, and push button, to name a few. The symbols for the spdt switch (Fig. 7-4) are the same as those of the spst except for the added connection.

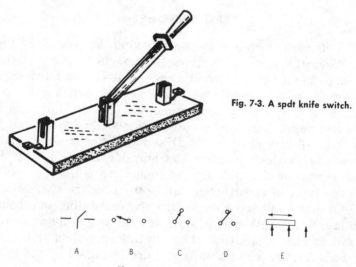

Fig. 7-3. A spdt knife switch.

Fig. 7-4. Spdt switch symbols.

DOUBLE-POLE SWITCHES

To control two separate circuits with a single switch, a double-pole unit is needed. It comprises two sections, each like the single-pole type shown previously, that are mechanically but not electrically connected. For instance, a *double-pole, single-throw* (dpst) knife switch consists of two blades, each of which can be connected to one set of terminals. The two blades are connected, or ganged, together (by an insulating material) so that when one is moved, the other automatically follows. Fig. 7-5 shows the symbols used to denote dpst

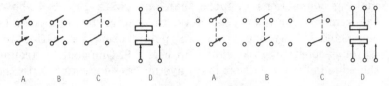

A   B   C   D   A   B   C   D

Fig. 7-5. Dpst switch symbols.   **Fig. 7-6. Dpdt switch symbols.**

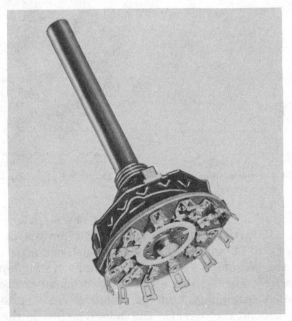

Courtesy Centralab, Electronics Div. of Globe-Union, Inc.

Fig. 7-7. A typical wafer switch.

switches. The dashed line indicates that the two arms are mechanically but not electrically connected.

By adding another set of terminals to the two-bladed knife switch so that the two mechanically connected blades make contact in either of two positions, it becomes a *double-pole, double-throw* (dpdt) switch. Fig. 7-6 shows the symbols for this type.

WAFER SWITCHES

The wafer switch shown in Fig. 7-7 is very popular for making connections to more than one point. Fig. 7-8 shows the symbols for one type. Here, the center terminal can be connected to any one of the six points around it. Often the wafer is constructed as shown in Fig. 7-9. One contact around the edge is longer so that it always makes connection with the

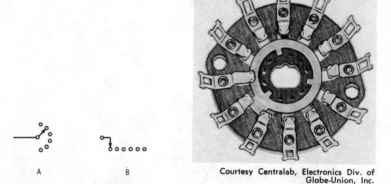

A   B

Courtesy Centralab, Electronics Div. of
Globe-Union, Inc.

Fig. 7-8. Single-pole, six-position switch symbols.

Fig. 7-9. A typical switch wafer.

circular ring in the center. Notice that one point on the ring extends out farther than the rest. As the switch is rotated, this point will be connected to each contact, one after another, around the outside. This, then, is actually a *single-pole, 12-throw* switch. Fig. 7-10 shows the most common symbol for it. The arrows extending from the small circles represent the contacts around the outside. The longest arrow is the longest contact. The ring is deliberately drawn so that it does not touch the arrowheads except at the long contact and at the point of extension on the ring. As the switch is rotated, this extension contacts each arrowhead in turn. The symbol is usually pictured as being viewed from the shaft end, and the terminals are numbered clockwise, as shown in Fig. 7-10. If the wafer is being pictured from the rear, the numbers will be numbered counterclockwise, of course.

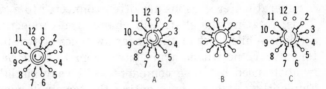

Fig. 7-10. A single-pole, twelve-position wafer-switch symbol.

Fig. 7-11. Wafer switch symbols.

A single-section wafer switch can be used when two or more circuits must be switched in and out at the same time. By making some points wider on the rotating ring, certain connections can be made between them and the stationary contacts. The ring may also be broken instead of solid so that one half will serve some of the stationary contacts, and the other half the remainder. For instance, symbol A in Fig. 7-11 shows a switch in which terminals 2 and 3 are connected to terminal 5, and terminals 7 and 9 to terminal 11. The arrow at the center indicates the direction the center portion moves when the switch is rotated. Rotating the switch one position will connect terminals 3 and 4 to terminal 5, and terminals 8 and 10 to terminal 11. Any number of connections can be made by such switches, each depending on the construction of the shorting ring. Two other possibilities are shown in symbols B and C.

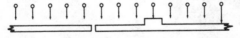

Fig. 7-12. Another method of representing a wafer switch.

Another method of showing a wafer switch is shown in Fig. 7-12. Here the switch is laid out horizontally. The bar below the row of arrowheads represents the inner shorting ring (which for illustrative purposes has been straightened out and broken). The jagged lines at the ends of the bar signify the broken bar. In the actual switch, the two ends are connected at this point. As the switch is rotated, the bar moves along and makes connections to the various contacts. The principal advantage of depicting the switch in this manner is that components connected across the various contacts can be shown more easily.

Several wafer sections are often connected to a single shaft. Thus, rotating the shaft will change the connections at each section. While most of the wafer switches shown in this chapter have 12 positions, many have from 18 to 24 or more. The symbols used by some companies will vary slightly. For example, the numbers representing the terminals may be placed within the circles. Nevertheless, all symbols will be very similar to the ones shown here.

PUSH-BUTTON SWITCHES

Sometimes the general switch symbol in Fig. 7-2 is utilized for the familiar push-button switch of Fig. 7-13. Symbol A in Fig. 7-14 is more widely used, however. The vertical por-

Fig. 7-13. A push-button switch.

tion represents the button; when pushed, it moves the bar down to make connection across the contacts, represented by the two circles. The same switch is also shown by symbol B. Here, the arrowheads represent the contacts. Both symbols A and B represent a normally open switch. If the switch is normally closed, pushing the button will open the circuit. Symbols C and D denote this type of switch.

A push-button switch can also be of the double-pole variety, as shown by symbol E. Here, pushing the button closes two circuits. Symbol F represents a switch which opens one circuit and closes another when the button is pushed. Many other types of switching are possible with switches like that of Fig. 7-15. For this type switch, the symbol will be made up using symbols like those of Fig. 7-14, except to show the actual arrangement of the contacts. Usually the dashed line will be used to indicate the various sections operated by a single push button.

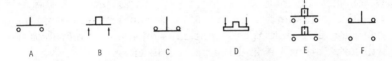

Fig. 7-14. Push-button switch symbols.

Fig. 7-15. A bank of push-button switches.

Courtesy Centralab, Electronics Div. of Globe-Union, Inc.

Code Letters

Switches may be designated by several different letters. The more common are *S*, *SW*, *M*, and *E*. In addition, the letters *WS* are sometimes used to indicate a wafer switch.

RELAYS

All the switches discussed previously were actuated by either rotating or sliding a knob, pushing a button, or some other mechanical movement. A relay is an automatic switch,

Courtesy Cornell-Dubilier Electric Corp.

Fig. 7-16. Typical general-purpose relays.

which may or may not require a physical action to be activated. For instance a relay could be connected into a photo-
electric-cell circuit. When light falls on the cell, more current
will flow through it and the relay will close.

A typical relay (Fig. 7-16) consists of a coil of wire wound
around an iron core, and two contacts. The relay becomes energized as current flows through the coil and causes its core
to act as an electromagnet. One of the contacts, being movable,
is attracted by this electromagnet, and in moving toward it,
touches the other (stationary) contact, completing the circuit.
When current through the coil decreases below a certain

STATIONARY
CONTACTS

MOVABLE
CONTACT

COIL

Courtesy Potter & Brumfield Div. of AMF, Inc.

Fig. 7-17. A general-purpose relay.

amount, a spring returns the contact to its original position. Just as there are many types of switches, there are also relays of many types and shapes to fit a mulitude of applications. A few of them are pictured in Fig. 7-16. A general-purpose relay is shown in Fig. 7-17 with the main parts called out.

The symbol for a simple relay is given at A in Fig. 7-18. The bar at the top of the symbol is the movable contact, and the arm with the arrowhead is the stationary one. The relay coil is represented by a wire wrapped around a rectangle (representing the core). The dashed line (sometimes omitted) signifies that the core attracts the movable element. Another method of showing the same relay is by symbol B; here, the regular iron-core coil symbol is used to represent the relay coil.

The relays in symbols A and B are both single-pole, single-throw units. All types of relays are available, however. For example, symbol C shows a single-pole, double-throw unit. The movable contact completes the circuit to the upper stationary contact. This is called the de-energized position (no current flowing through the coil). When current does flow, the movable contact is pulled down, opening the upper circuit and closing the lower one.

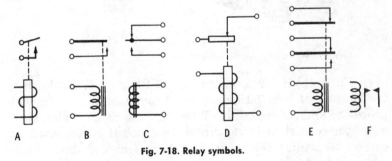

Fig. 7-18. Relay symbols.

To simplify circuit layout, the connections to the relay are sometimes brought out different sides, as shown in D. The circuit between the two contacts in this relay is normally closed: When energized, the movable contact is pulled down and opens the circuit. Sometimes the letters *NC* (for normally closed) or *NO* (for normally open) are placed beside the contacts on the schematic to signify the de-energized position.

A single relay coil may operate more than one movable arm at the same time. Symbol E depicts a two-section relay. The top part is a single-pole, single-throw section which is normally closed. The bottom part is a single-pole, double-throw unit which is normally connected to the upper contact. A somewhat different way of representing a relay is given at F.

There are innumerable possibilities in the types of relays, but their operation is obvious from examining the contacts. Just remember that the relay is normally shown in its de-energized position, and that energizing the relay will cause the position of the bar to move toward the coil.

Solid-State Relay

A more recent development is the "solid-state" relay of Fig. 7-19. This device does not have actual contacts like the magnetic relays discussed previously. Instead, the actual switching

Fig. 7-19. A solid-state relay.

Courtesy Potter & Brumfield Div. of AMF, Inc.

device is a thyristor as discussed in Chapter 6. Enclosed in the housing of Fig. 7-19 are several components. The input is processed and connected to a light emitting diode, which glows when the conditions in the circuit to which it is connected are correct to actuate the relay. This light emitting diode shines on a photo detector which then conducts causing the trigger current to be applied to the thyristor. Thus, the output is isolated from the input by the simple LED and photo detector arrangement, just as the electromagnet isolated the input from the switching contacts in the conventional relay. Other components are added inside the housing of Fig. 7-19 to prevent false triggering of the thyristor by pulses on the line, etc.

The solid-state relay is represented in schematics by a drawing of the individual components within the housing and the entire unit enclosed in dashed or a solid-line box. At other times the "black-box" approach may be used. That is, a square or rectangular box will be used to represent the relay. The internal circuitry will not be shown and just the input and output connection to the box will be given.

The most common letters for designating relays on schematic diagrams are *K*, *RE*, *RL*, *M*, and *E*.

QUESTIONS

1. What is the basic purpose of a switch?
2. What type of switch is most commonly used as the on-off switch for a radio?
3. What type of switch does the abbreviation spdt indicate?
4. What is the purpose of the switch in Question 3?
5. What is a relay?
6. What does a dashed line between two points on a switch symbol indicate?
7. What is the purpose of the coil in a relay?
8. What are three of the code letters used to designate switches on schematics?
9. Draw the symbol for a double-pole, double-throw switch.
10. Draw the symbol for a single-pole, double-throw relay.

CHAPTER 8

Miscellaneous Components

Nearly all the components discussed in the previous chapters will be found in any one piece of electronic equipment. In most cases, more than one of each will be included. Even so, it is exceedingly rare that such equipment can be constructed from those components alone. Instead, many other items are necessary for its operation.

Don't think that because they have been classified as "miscellaneous," the components to be discussed in this chapter are less important. This is not true. For instance, what good would a radio be without a speaker? The reason for the miscellaneous classification is that *all* the items in this chapter are not necessarily found in *every* piece of equipment.

ANTENNAS

No piece of transmitting or receiving equipment is complete without an antenna. At the transmitter, it is the final unit in the system. From it, the electromagnetic waves are "sent out" through the air to the receiver. Here, the antenna is the first unit in the system, intercepting these electromagnetic waves and conveying or coupling them to the input. Sometimes the antenna is not an integral part of the equipment, but is mounted externally (on a roof, tower, etc.). In such a case the antenna symbol may not be included on the schematic, but only the terminals where it is to be connected (see next chapter).

Symbols

Fig. 8-1 shows the symbols commonly employed for antennas. Symbols A, B, C, and D generally designate external antennas.

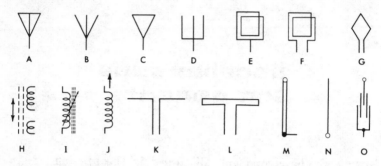

Fig. 8-1. Antenna symbols.

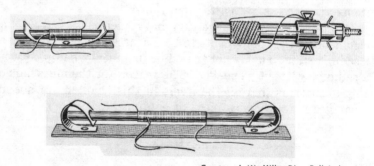

Courtesy J. W. Miller Div., Bell Industries

Fig. 8-2. Ferrite loop antennas.

Three methods of depicting the familiar loop antenna are shown in E, F, and G. (A loop antenna is a coiled length of wire usually fastened flat against the back of the cabinet.) Other versions of this symbol may be employed, but all will resemble this general layout. Another type of built-in antenna may use either symbol E, F, G, H, I, or J. This is called a *ferrite-loop antenna* (Fig. 8-2). It is actually a coil of wire wound around a ferrite core. Besides having the advantage of being very sensitive to weak signals, it may also be tunable. A length of wire attached to the unit may be stretched out for additional pickup. Notice that symbols H, I, and J are the same as those for a coil, which this type of antenna actually is. Some versions are not tunable. In this case the arrow is omitted.

Methods of indicating tv antennas are shown by symbols K through O in Fig. 8-1. Symbol K is often used for any type, but actually represents a dipole—the basic tv antenna. Symbol L is another basic tv antenna—the folded dipole. The symbols at M, N, and O are for a monopole antenna (the single telescoping rod built into portable tv receivers). Two of these symbols may be used on some receiver schematics, signifying two telescoping elements.

Code Letters

Since all antennas—no matter how constructed—are so similar in function to a coil, many manufacturers use the letter L to designate them. Others prefer E or M.

SPEAKERS

The speaker is the final link in the chain of stages in a radio receiver or amplifier and in the sound system of a tv receiver. Its purpose is to convert the electrical signals, which vary in step with the sound to be reproduced, into the actual sounds.

A cutaway view showing the construction details of a typical speaker is given in Fig. 8-3. The speaker operates as follows: The signal voltage is connected to the terminals on the speaker frame (called the basket) and is carried from there to the voice coil by leads. Thus, a current which varies in step with the signal flows through the voice coil. The permanent magnet interacts with the magnetic lines of force set up by the current. When the current flows in one direction, the voice coil moves backward along the pole piece; and when current flows in the opposite direction, it moves forward. The voice coil is held over the magnet by a fiber disc called the *spider*, which is also connected to the cone. Therefore, as the voice coil moves, the cone does also, alternately expanding and com-

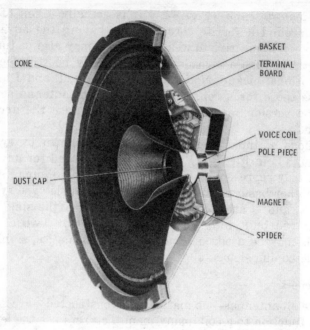

CONE

BASKET

TERMINAL BOARD

VOICE COIL

POLE PIECE

DUST CAP

MAGNET

SPIDER

Courtesy Utah Electronics

Fig. 8-3. A typical public address speaker.

Fig. 8-4. A three-way hi-fi speaker.

Courtesy Utah Electronics

pressing the air in front of it. Sound waves are nothing more than cycles of rarefied and compressed air, so the sound we hear is actually the disturbances produced by the cone.

The size of the cone affects the range of tones which the speaker will reproduce. In general, a smaller speaker is better for the reproduction of the higher tones, and larger cone for the lower tones. Often two or three speakers are used to reproduce the entire range of tones. Another approach is pictured in Fig. 8-4. This is a 3-way speaker where the large cone at the outside is used to reproduce the low tones, and the separate tweeter unit in the center reproduces the higher tones.

Symbols

Many different symbols are used for speakers, as shown in Fig. 8-5.

Sometimes the symbol for a single speaker is also used to depict the coaxial type of Fig. 8-4. At other times, two speaker symbols enclosed in a dashed-line box may be employed. Other minor variations of the symbols shown in Fig. 8-5 may be encountered; however, they will usually resemble those shown in this illustration.

Code Letters

The letters S, SP, SPK, LS, E, and M are most commonly employed by the various companies to designate speakers.

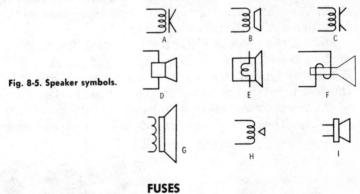

Fig. 8-5. Speaker symbols.

FUSES

Unless some protection is provided, a short or other malfunction could destroy an entire piece of electronic equipment. This protection is provided by fuses, some typical types being

Courtesy Littelfuse, Inc.

Fig. 8-6. Typical fuses and fuse holders.

shown in Fig. 8-6. When a circuit draws too much current, the metal strip or wire inside the fuse melts, interrupting the excessive flow.

There are many types of fuses as indicated in the photo. Some are designed to open the instant the current exceeds the rated value. Others do not open if a momentary surge of current higher than the rated value flows through them, unless the surge is prolonged.

Some are enclosed in a ceramic instead of glass covering. Fuses may be rated at .01 amp or less (used to protect meter circuits); others are designed to withstand several amperes. Other fuses have leads extending from their ends so they can be soldered directly into the circuit.

Most of the fuses in Fig. 8-6 are inserted into holders. Some holders are shown in the lower left of the photo.

Another type of fuse and holder is shown in Fig. 8-7. Here, the fuse is twisted to lock it in place in the holder. The length of the fuse and the width of the locking tabs differ according to rating. Thus, the wrong size of fuse cannot be inserted.

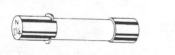

Courtesy Bussman Mfg. Div., McGraw-Edison Co.

Fig. 8-7. A n-type fuse and its holder.

Two types of semiconductor fuses are pictured in Fig. 8-8. The ones shown in Fig. 8-8A are available in sizes from 5 to 800 amperes. They feature a ceramic body which is designed to prevent charring and arcing when the fuse blows. The ones shown in Fig. 8-8B have an indicator to show the condition of the fuse.

Fuse Symbols

Symbols A and B in Fig. 8-9 are used by nearly every company to designate fuses. The only difference between the two is the addition of the circle in B to denote the terminals. The symbol at C is sometimes used for a special type of fuse in which a chemical is used in place of a wire.

Code Letters

Most companies designate fuses by the letter F on their schematics, although some prefer M or E. The rating usually appears on the schematic, alongside the fuse symbol and, if a slow-blow type, this fact will usually be noted, too.

CIRCUIT BREAKERS

The circuit breaker performs the same function as a fuse, but does not destroy itself in case of an overload. It merely opens two contacts, which are restored by pressing a button. The circuit breakers in modern home electrical systems are a familiar application of this principle. Other circuit breakers are made for the small value of current in tv receivers or similar equipment. Fig. 8-10 shows two of the many types of circuit breakers.

There are two basic principles of operation for circuit breakers. In the thermal type, the current heats a metal strip which bends enough to open the contacts when the current reaches a predetermined value. When the strip cools, the contacts can be closed again by pushing the reset button. In the other type, an electromagnet (formed by a coil of wire) has sufficient strength to attract one of the contacts and open the circuit when the current reaches the prescribed limit. Again, pushing the reset button closes the circuit. (However, it will open again if the overload still exists.) Some units combine the thermal and magnetic principles.

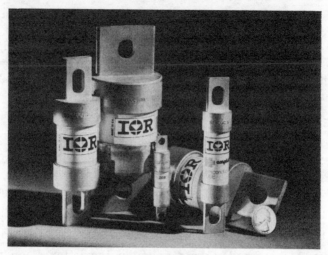

(A) Heavy duty type.

(B) Indicator type.

Courtesy International Rectifier

Fig. 8-8. Semiconductor fuses.

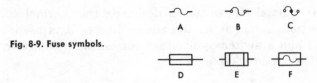

Fig. 8-9. Fuse symbols.

Courtesy Potter & Brumfield Div. of AMF, Inc.

Courtesy Littelfuse, Inc.

(A) Panel mounted.

(B) Chassis mounted.

Fig. 8-10. Circuit breakers.

Symbols

Several symbols are used to represent circuit breakers. The ones at A, B, C, and D in Fig. 8-11 denote both thermal and magnetic types. Symbol A is sometimes altered to show the method of operation. For example, adding a slant line to the curved portion of the symbol as in E indicates a switch-type breaker. Symbol F indicates a push-pull unit, and symbol G a push-push breaker.

The symbols for thermal units are given at H and I in Fig. 8-11. They are a combination of symbol A and a square

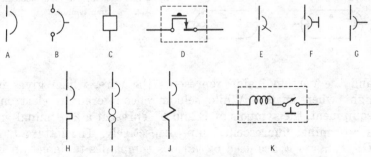

Fig. 8-11. Circuit breaker symbols.

or two partial circles which designate the thermal action. If the action is magnetic, the zigzag line in J is used instead. A coil and a switch symbol are combined to depict the magnetic circuit breaker in K.

Code Letters

The most common code letters for circuit breakers are *CB*, *M*, *RC*, and *E*. Sometimes the letter *F* is used, however. This is a carryover from the fuse which the breaker replaces.

LAMPS

Two types of lamps are generally employed for lighting the dials and other indicators in practically all types of electronic equipment. The first is a regular incandescent type similar to the common flashlight bulb. The other obtains its lighting properties from a rare gas, such as neon.

Incandescent Lamps

The incandescent lamp is used where illumination, rather than a warning signal, is needed. For example, many radio and tv dials have lamps behind them to make the markings visible. In other equipment a lamp may be placed behind a jeweled bead which glows to indicate that the unit is on. The symbols for incandescent dial lamps are given at A through D in Fig. 8-12. The circle depicts the glass envelope of the bulb;

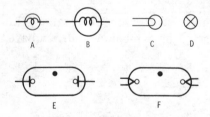

Fig. 8-12. Incandescent- and fluorescent-lamp symbols.

and the portion inside represents the wire, which gives off light when heated. While seldom encountered in electronic equipment, the symbols at E and F represent a 2-terminal and a 4-terminal fluorescent lamp, respectively. The letters *I*, *B*, *DS*, *PL*, and *E* are used by various companies to depict an incandescent lamp. Others may also be employed.

Neon Lamps

The neon lamp gives off only a soft red glow when lit. Its widest application, therefore, is as an indicator. It consists of two plates, called electrodes, separated by the neon gas.

The symbols for neon lamps (Fig. 8-13) all depict these two electrodes. The only difference is in the manner in which they are drawn and in the dot (which always symbolizes gas) inside the envelope. Symbol E is for ac lamps only, and symbol F is its dc counterpart. The same code letters designate neon as well as incandescent lamps. *I, B,* and *DS* are the most common, however. Sometimes the letters *NE* (for neon) are also employed.

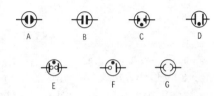

Fig. 8-13. Neon lamp symbols.

BATTERIES

Batteries power many types of portable equipment. Essentially, all batteries consist of two dissimilar materials in a solution—either plates immersed in an acid, as in the automobile storage battery; or a carbon rod and a zinc container with a solid material between them, as in a flashlight cell. Other batteries employ nickel-cadmium, alkaline-magnesium, and mercury in their construction. The same symbols are used for all.

A cell, often incorrectly called a battery, is the basic unit. A battery is two or more cells used together to provide the desired voltage or current. For example, a 12.6-volt storage battery contains six cells, each supplying 2.1 volts.

The two dissimilar plates form the symbol for a cell, as shown in A of Fig. 8-14. This symbol is practically universal in acceptance. The shorter bar represents the negative, and the longer bar the positive, plate. Often the "+" and "−" signs are also included on the symbol, as shown; sometimes only the plus sign is included. Others eliminate both signs.

Sets of bars are added to depict multicell units, as shown in B and C—but don't be misled into believing the number of pairs of bars always conforms to the actual number of cells in the battery. Sometimes they do, but usually no more than four or five sets of bars are employed, no matter how many cells they represent. Symbol D denotes a battery with taps at various points, and E a battery with a variable tap. Such symbols are rather rare, however.

Letters *B*, *BT*, *E*, and *M* are the most common for identifying batteries on schematics.

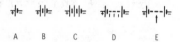

A   B   C   D   E

Fig. 8-14. Battery symbols.

CRYSTALS

Crystals (Fig. 8-15) are made from materials, such as quartz, which have the unique property of generating a voltage when pressure is applied to them, called the piezoelectric effect. Conversely, when an alternating voltage is applied, they will bend or twist in synchronism with the variation. By cutting a crystal at various angles and to different dimensions, and by making electrical connections to it with a metal plate on each side (called a holder), the crystal can be made to oscillate or vibrate at which is called its *resonant frequency*.

Once a crystal starts oscillating, only a very small force is required at the same frequency to obtain large-amplitude os-

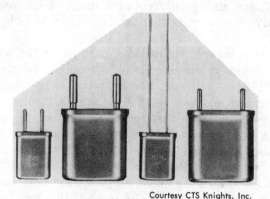

Courtesy CTS Knights, Inc.
Fig. 8-15. Piezoelectric crystals.

cillations. These oscillations of alternating voltage are often connected to the grid circuit of a crystal-oscillator stage. Since a crystal will oscillate at only one frequency (determined by its dimensions), the frequency of the crystal-oscillator stage will remain constant. Crystals are also used as filters for tuning amplifiers so only a certain desired band of frequencies will pass and others will be rejected.

The symbols for a crystal in Fig. 8-16 illustrate its physical construction. The two bars represent the holder, and the rectangle or slanted lines, the crystal element.

The letters Y, M, and X are used by various companies to identify crystals on their schematics.

Fig. 8-16. Crystal symbols.

A   B   C   D

MICROPHONES

Sound waves, as they exist, cannot be boosted in strength. Nor can they be mixed directly with the signal at a radio station and transmitted over the airwaves. True, a megaphone can direct the sound to a certain point, but the total power contained will not be increased.

Before sound waves can be amplified, they must be changed into an electrical signal. This signal can then be put to a number of uses—it can be boosted in strength by an amplifier and converted back to sound by a speaker, mixed with the radio or tv station signal (called "modulating"), applied to the head of a tape recorder to record the signal on tape, etc.

A microphone (Fig. 8-17) changes sound waves into a varying electrical signal. Thus, its purpose is just the opposite from that of the speaker discussed earlier in this chapter. A speaker, however, will work as a microphone. Most intercom systems use a conventioinal speaker which, by proper switching, also acts as a microphone.

One type of microphone employs a coil which moves in a magnetic field and thereby converts sound into electrical waves. As the sound waves strike the diaphragm, the coil movement induces a voltage in the coil. Such microphones are called *dynamic* or *moving-coil* types.

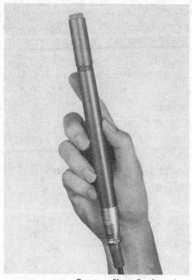

Fig. 8-17. A dynamic microphone.

Courtesy Shure Brothers, Inc.

Several other principles are used for microphones. The carbon type consists of a brass cup filled with compressed carbon granules. A diaphragm connected to the cup is moved back and forth by the sound waves. The movement changes the pressure on the granules and hence the resistance of the carbon to the flow of current through it. Another microphone operates on the capacitor principle—the sound waves move a plate back and forth with respect to a fixed plate and thereby change the capacitance.

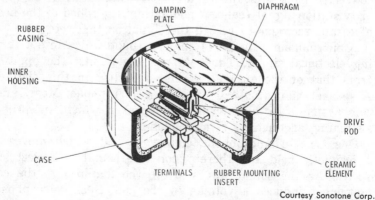

Courtesy Sonotone Corp.

Fig. 8-18. Construction details of a ceramic microphone.

124

Fig. 8-18 shows the construction of a *ceramic* microphone. Here the sound enters the louvered plate at the top and strikes the diaphragm, moving it back and forth. The ceramic element (barium titanate), connected to the diaphragm by the drive rod, exhibits properties similar to those of the crystal discussed earlier in this chapter. That is, as the pressure of the sound waves bends the ceramic unit, a voltage is generated. The resulting current is transferred, via the terminal at the bottom, to the amplifier. The unit shown in Fig. 8-18 is enclosed in a housing for protection.

Some microphones employ crystals (Rochelle salts are the most common) instead of the ceramic elements. However, they are more susceptible to damage by high temperatures and humidity than the ceramic units.

The most common symbols for a microphone are shown in A, B, and C of Fig. 8-19. When these symbols are used, the type (crystal, magnetic, etc.), is usually designated by a note beside the symbol. Symbols D, E, and F represent crystal

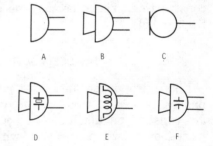

Fig. 8-19. Microphone symbols.

(ceramic), dynamic, and capacitor microphones, respectively. The microphone symbol is often omitted from schematics because it usually is not an integral part of the unit. Instead, only the terminals to which it is connected are shown.

The letters *M*, *MK*, *MIC*, or *E* are the most popular for microphones. Often, no code letter is used. Instead, the type of microphone is written out beside the symbol.

TRANSDUCERS

The microphones described in the preceding are designed to pick up sounds that we can hear and convert them to electrical waves. Other devices are very similar, but are designed to respond to sounds we cannot hear. A common example of this application is the use of ultrasonic sounds for remote control of a television receiver. In this application the unit is called a transducer, or ultrasonic microphone. (Actually the term "transducer" describes any device for transferring the flow of energy from one or more systems to one or more other systems. Thus, a speaker is also a transducer; a sonar

Fig. 8-20. Ultrasonic transducer symbols.

pickup is another transducer. The application of the term "transducer" to ultrasonics is quite common, however.) Fig. 8-20 shows some of the symbols used to depict ultrasonic transducers. As with microphones, many materials are used for construction. The type may be designated by a note beside the symbol.

HEADSETS AND EARPHONES

Like the speakers discussed previously, the headset or earphones convert a varying voltage into sound. Some of them are constructed much like a speaker. Usually, two coils are placed over two pole pieces which are permanent magnets. These pole pieces attract a metal diaphragm suspended over them. As the current through the coils varies, the magnetic field it sets up is alternately added to and subtracted from the field of the permanent magnets. This changing field moves the diaphragm back and forth in step with the voltage.

Other types of headsets have crystal or ceramic elements. They operate like the microphone discussed previously, except in reverse. That is, a varying voltage is applied to the crystal or ceramic slab, which in turn moves the diaphragm back and forth.

The two basic symbols for headsets and earphones are given by A and B in Fig. 8-21. Symbol C is for a double headset. Additional circles are sometimes placed inside the symbol, as

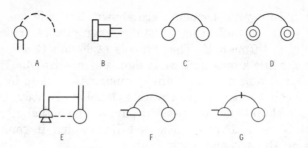

Fig. 8-21. Earphone, headphone, and headset symbols.

shown by D. Symbols E and F, a combination of those in Fig. 8-19 and A in Fig. 8-21, designate a handset (a combination microphone and earphone) used in telephone and some intercom systems. The addition of a line on the connecting arc in symbol F, as shown at G, signifies a push-to-talk switch on the handset.

PHONO PICKUPS

The phono cartridge (Fig. 8-22) converts into electrical signals the vibrations produced by the variations in a record groove. It bears a close resemblance to the microphone, where the variations in sound waves are converted into electrical signals. Many symbols have been devised for depicting the phono cartridge. Since some are monaural and others are for stereo, and since some have one needle and others two, differences in indicating them are inevitable. Symbols A and B in Fig. 8-23 are similar except that B represents a stereo car-

Courtesy Shure Brothers, Inc.

Fig. 8-22. Phono cartridge.

tridge. Two crystal elements are shown, but only one needle. Other ways of indicating crystal or ceramic cartridges are given by C through E. The symbols at F and G are general symbols, while a magnetic cartridge is symbolized by H. Symbol D can also be made to signify a magnetic pickup by substituting a coil symbol for the crystal symbol on its body. Usually, when a pickup is not an integral part of the actual circuit, no symbol is used; instead, a socket into which it connects is shown on the schematic.

In place of the code letter, an identifying note is often placed beside the symbol for a pickup. When employed, the letters *M, P,* and *PU* are the most popular.

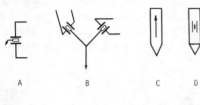

Fig. 8-23. Phono cartridge symbols.

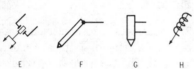

TAPE HEADS

In a magnetic tape recorder the heads perform three functions. The first function is essentially the same as that of the phono pickup. The head converts the variations in the recording to an electrical signal which corresponds to the sound that has been recorded. This electrical signal is then amplified before it is applied to a speaker, where the electrical signal is converted to sound. The difference between a tape head and a phono pickup is that on a phonograph record, variations are cut in the groove to correspond to the signal. In a tape recorder, a varying magnetic field is applied to the tape which holds this magnetic pattern. As the tape passes the head, a signal is developed in the head circuit which varies in step with the signal originally used to magnetize the tape.

The second function provided by magnetic heads is to record the signal on the tape. Essentially this is the reverse of

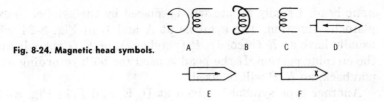

Fig. 8-24. Magnetic head symbols.

the pickup. Here the signal is applied to the head. As the tape passes the head a varying magnetic field is set up in the tape corresponding to this signal. Often the same head is used for recording and playback, and the connections to the head are changed by a switching arrangement.

The third function of heads is erasing. Magnetic tape can be used over and over. Once a pattern is recorded on the tape, it will remain on the tape until it is erased by bringing it in contact with a magnetic field. This magnetic field can be dc or a high-frequency ac, but the ac is more common. Most tape recorders have a head which contacts the tape just ahead of the recording head. Called the erase head, it removes any signal on the tape just before the new signal is recorded. During playback, no signal is applied to this head so the signal will not be removed. Fig. 8-24 shows the symbols for tape-recording heads. The ones at A and B show a combination of a coil and a circular element. This is similar to the actual construction of a magnetic head, as shown in the photo of Fig. 8-25. A coil is sometimes used by itself to show a mag-

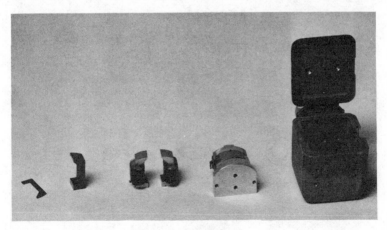

Fig. 8-25. Magnetic heads.

netic head. Usually a note will be placed by the symbol to explain its function. The symbols at A and B in Fig. 8-24 will usually have an *R* (record), *P* (playback), or *E* (erase) inside the circular portion. If the head is used for both recording and playback, an *R/P* will be used.

Another type symbol is given at D, E, and F in Fig. 8-24. The one at D, with the arrow pointing away from the tip signifies a playback head. The symbol at E is for a record head and the "x" in the symbol at F identifies an erase head. By combining D and E and having arrows pointing in both directions, the symbol for a record-playback head is produced.

ROTATING MACHINES

Although not classed as electronic equipment, motors, generators, dynamotors, etc., are sometimes included on schematic diagrams. Phonographs and tape recorders are examples of equipment using motors.

Motors

The basic symbol for a motor is an *M*, the letters *MOT*, or the word *MOTOR* placed either alongside or inside a circle, as shown by A in Fig. 8-26.

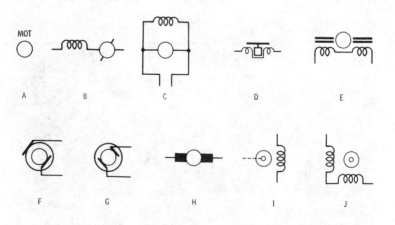

Fig. 8-26. Motor symbols.

Where it is desirable to show the connections to the motor, symbols B and C may be used. In symbol B, the field coil is in series with the armature, while symbol C shows it in parallel. (The coil symbol depicts the field, and the circle the armature.) Two methods of showing phonograph motors are illustrated by symbols D and E. Some other representative methods are depicted in F through J. In each instance, the symbol is drawn to conform with the motor connections.

Generators

In general, symbols for generators are the same as for motors, except the letter G, the letters GEN, or the word $GENERATOR$ will be used, of course.

SOLENOIDS

A solenoid is an electrical device which provides some mechanical action, such as closing a valve or sounding a door chime, when a voltage source is connected to it (by pushing a button, for example).

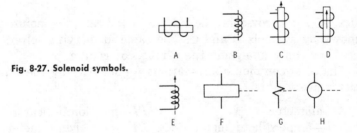

Fig. 8-27. Solenoid symbols.

A solenoid consists of a coil surrounding a movable iron core attached to a spring. When current flows through the coil, the core is either attracted farther into the coil or repelled partially from it. The movement of the core actuates the device to which it is connected. When the current through the coil ceases to flow, the spring returns the core to its original position.

As you have probably guessed, the symbol for a solenoid is often like that for a coil with a core, as shown by A and B in Fig. 8-27. An arrow will sometimes be added, as shown in C,

D, and E, to depict the fact that the core is movable. Other symbols sometimes used are given at F, G, and H.

METERS

Meters (Fig. 8-28) are sometimes included in electronic equipment so that operating conditions or other information can be monitored. They are often depicted by symbol A in Fig. 8-29, accompanied by identifying letters inside or along-

Courtesy Triplett Corp.

Fig. 8-28. Panel meters.

side it. An arrow may be added to indicate the pointer, as shown by symbols B and C. The same identifying letters are used, but only alongside the symbol, of course.

The most common abbreviations for identifying the type of meter are:

A—ammeter
AH—ampere-hour meter
CRO—oscilloscope
D—demand meter
DB—decibel meter
F—frequency meter
G—galvanometer
I—indicating meter
MA—milliammeter
NM—noise meter
OHM—ohmmeter
PF—power-factor meter
PH—phasemeter

PI—position indicator
REC—recording meter
SY—synchroscope
t°—temperature meter
TLM—telemeter
UA or μA—microammeter
V—voltmeter
VA—volt-ammeter
VI—volume indicator
VU—volume-unit meter
W—wattmeter
WH—watt-hour meter

Fig. 8-29. Meter symbols.

OTHER SYMBOLS

Up to this point we have discussed practically every component used in electronic equipment. Fig. 8-30 illustrates the symbols used for some items which will occasionally be found, particularly in specialized equipment. Symbol A is for a spark plate used in automobile radios. It consists of a metal plate placed alongside the chassis and separated by an insulating material. Three methods of depicting lightning arresters are shown by B, C, and D. Symbol E is for a bell, while F depicts a buzzer. Symbol G is for a telegraph key. Symbol H is for a telegraph sounder. The symbol at I is for a thermocouple temperature measuring device.

A manufacturer will sometimes want to show a drawing of a large installation, but not every circuit component. On this type of diagram, an entire amplifier is indicated by a triangle, as shown by A in·Fig. 8-31. For more complicated circuits, two inputs and a single output will be shown as in B, or two inputs and two outputs as in C.

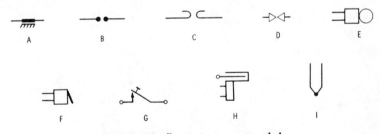

Fig. 8-30. Miscellaneous component symbols.

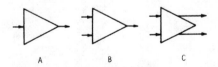

Fig. 8-31. Amplifier symbols.

QUESTIONS

1. What is the purpose of a speaker?
2. What circuit element destroys itself when it performs its intended purpose?
3. What are the two types of lamps used in entertainment-type equipment?
4. What is the difference between a cell and a battery?
5. Name three types of microphones.
6. Draw the symbol for a headset.
7. Draw the symbol for a voltmeter.
8. Draw the symbol for a crystal.
9. Draw a battery symbol and indicate the polarity.
10. What does this symbol indicate?

CHAPTER 9

Connecting the Components

All components are useless unless they can be interconnected. There are many ways to do this. One—the printed circuit—was a contributing factor in the development of the "personal-sized" transistor radio.

WIRES

The most widely known method of connection, of course, is by means of a wire. It can be an actual wire run between two points, or the wire (more commonly called lead) of a component. Nevertheless, the two are indicated in the same way on the schematic.

As you probably know, a line denotes a wire or a component lead. There are three methods of showing whether two leads are connected or not. The first is illustrated by A in Fig. 9-1. The vertical line at the left intersects the horizontal line, indicating in this system that they are connected. Now notice that the lead at the right has a half-circle at the crossover point. The half-circle means that this wire (called a jumper) bypasses the horizontal line.

In the system at B, the dot placed at the point where the left vertical line crosses the horizontal denotes that the two lines are connected. Conversely, no dot at the intersection of the right vertical and the horizontal lines indicates no connection.

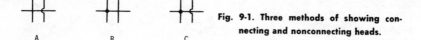

Fig. 9-1. Three methods of showing connecting and nonconnecting heads.

A   B   C

These two systems can be confusing if you don't know off hand which one is being used. In A, two crossed lines indicate a connection, whereas in B, they indicate just the opposite. For this reason, it is always best to carefully study the schematic first. If jumpers are used at some places, you know that the crossed lines indicate a connection. Dots at the point where some lines cross alert you to the fact that lines crossing without dots do not connect. The system at C in Fig. 9-1, actually a combination of the two previous systems, eliminates any chance of confusion. The dot (at the left) indicates that the two lines connect. To be on the safe side, the jumper (at the right) is also used to indicate no connection.

GROUND AND CHASSIS SYMBOLS

Three other symbols often seen on schematics are given in Fig. 9-2. Those at A, B, C, and D are referred to as ground symbols. Actually the term "ground" is a carryover from the early days of radio when the receiver was literally connected to the earth (ground). The term "earth" is used in British terminology to describe this point. Today the more popular symbol A designates a common-return point for all circuits. Otherwise, a line would have to be drawn to all of them. Imagine how cluttered up the schematic would be! All points exhibiting this symbol are considered connected.

Often, the ground symbol signifies the chassis of the equipment. Instead of the various points being connected by a wire, they are merely connected to the metal chassis. This is true except in ac/dc equipment, where doing so would necessitate connecting the chassis to one side of the power line. This would make the chassis "hot"; anyone touching it could receive a shock. In this type of circuit, the chassis is designated by the symbol at E in Fig. 9-2.

A   B   C   D   E

Fig. 9-2. Ground and chassis symbols.

Sometimes, particularly in high-fidelity equipment, a heavy copper conductor called a "bus bar" will be positioned near several stages and connected to ground. All circuits are then returned to ground through it instead of directly to the chassis. The advantage of such an arrangement is reduced hum. The bus bar may be indicated on the schematic by an extra heavy line.

OTHER METHODS OF DENOTING CONNECTIONS

Companies are constantly striving to make their schematics easier to read. A long, winding line is most difficult to follow around a schematic when the connections are remote and widely separated. Eliminating as many lines as possible is one way to simplify a schematic. For example, instead of drawing them from the voltage sources in a power supply to their destinations, an arrangement like that in A of Fig. 9-3 can be used. Each source is indicated by a dot and labeled with the voltage available at that point. Then, all other points

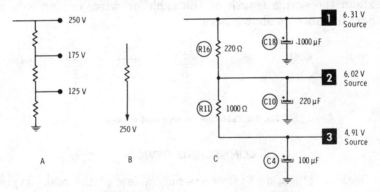

Fig. 9-3. Methods of showing voltage sources.

connected to this source are indicated by an arrow, circle, or dot and labeled with the voltage, as shown at B. Coded letters such as *A, B,* and *C* occasionally are used instead of listing the actual voltage. Another method is shown at C in Fig. 9-3. This is the output of a tape recorder power supply. The different voltages are designated by the 1, 2, and 3 in the black boxes. Any point on the schematic connected to this point will have the same black box and number.

Some companies employ triangles, squares, diamonds, and other geometric designs to signify connection between two points. Often, the source is indicated by a solid symbol, and the points connected to it by the outline of the same symbol.

Similar methods have been adopted for designating connections between points other than voltage sources. Usually, letters are employed—all points labeled with the same letter are assumed to be connected.

Sometimes two points are interconnected by a cable (several wires bundled together), usually designated by symbol A in Fig. 9-4. The ring surrounding all wires represents the outer covering of the cable, and may be placed at each end or in the center. If the cable is shielded, a ground symbol may be added to the symbol at A, as shown at B. Also, a dashed circle may be used, or a dashed line above and below the lines representing the wires, as shown at C and D. A ground symbol will be connected to the dashed lines, as shown at C and D. The same systems are also used for designating a single shielded lead, as shown by symbols E, F, and G. The dashed lines at G may extend the entire length of the cable or wire, or for only a short distance as shown here.

Fig. 9-4. Cable and shielded lead symbols.

CONNECTING DEVICES

Sockets, plugs, and jacks are only a few of the many types of connectors. All have one thing in common—a convenient means for connecting and disconnecting two points.

The symbol for connectors is usually an actual drawing of the device. Symbols A, B, and C in Fig. 9-5 are good examples; A and B are side views and C is an end view. Symbol D is for a socket. The symbol for a pronged unit (plug) is solid, and hollow for the open unit (the socket). The same system is used for most plug-and-socket combinations. Fig. 9-6 depicts only a few of them. In each instance, the symbols show the actual arrangement of the plug pins or socket openings.

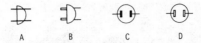

Fig. 9-5. Symbols for ac line-cord plugs.

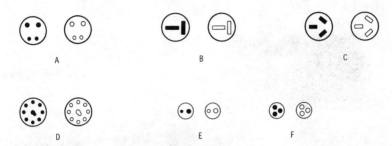

Fig. 9-6. Various plug and socket symbols.

Fig. 9-7 illustrates five methods of showing connections for single leads. Symbols A and B are for the familiar phono-type plug and socket found on the rear of many radio and tv receivers. Symbols C, D, and E all depict simple one-wire connectors. The arrowhead in symbol C is the plug and the remainder is the socket. Symbols D and E use the same solid and hollow representation explained before.

There are many plug and socket combinations as shown in Fig. 9-8. If the socket and plug contain so many connections that it would be difficult to show leads from all the pins, a different method is sometimes used. The various points may be arranged in a row and each pin and socket terminal numbered, as shown in Fig. 9-9. A separate drawing showing the

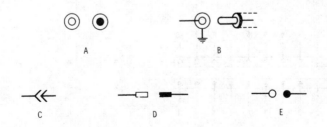

Fig. 9-7. Single-wire connector symbols.

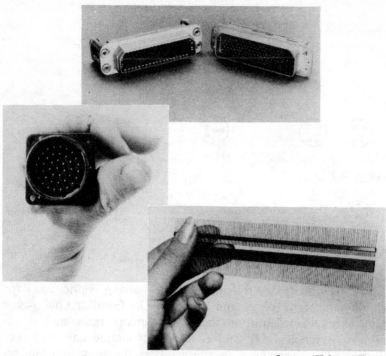

Courtesy ITT Cannon Electric

Fig. 9-8. Multiconductor connectors.

pin numbering and arrangement is usually included on the schematic also. Instead of the arrangement of Fig. 9-9, individual connections may be shown, as in C, D, and E of Fig. 9-7. Each is then labeled with the plug or socket number, followed by a dash and a number denoting the pin. Most of the time, plugs and sockets are not identified by code letters. When they

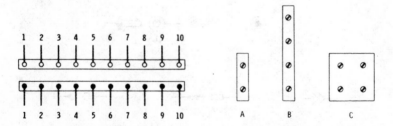

Fig. 9-9. One method of showing multicontact plugs and sockets.

Fig. 9-10. Terminal symbols.

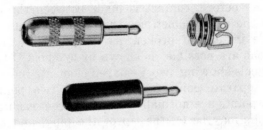

Courtesy Switchcraft, Inc.

Fig. 9-11. Typical plugs and jacks.

are, the letters *P* or *PL* (for plug) and *S* or *SK* (for socket), or *X* and *M* are the most popular.

Terminals for the antenna, speaker, etc., connections must also be shown on schematics. Fig. 9-10 shows some of the more common designations.

Jacks and their matching plugs (Fig. 9-11) are also used in many types of equipment, usually to make or break connections as the plug is inserted. Fig. 9-12 shows some typical symbols for jacks of this type. (The arrow shown with symbol A indicates the direction in which the plug is inserted, but is not a part of the symbol.) When inserted, the tip of the plug is connected to the upper terminal in symbol A. In B, the plug strikes the V-shaped portion connected to the upper terminal, forcing it up and disconnecting it from the center

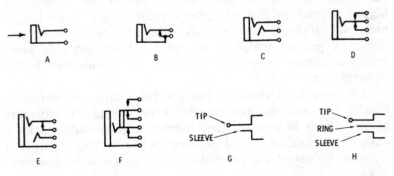

Fig. 9-12. Symbols for various types of jacks and plugs.

terminal. As before, contact is made between the upper terminal and the plug. Sometimes the plug will cause a contact to be made instead of broken, as in symbol C. Many other combinations are possible, as shown by symbols D through G.

The symbols showing two V-shaped elements indicate a jack with two separate connectors contacting two points of the plug. Both points are normally insulated from each other. For example, one may be on the tip of the plug, and the second on another portion called the ring.

The cross-hatched pattern of the symbol at F signifies that the two points to which they are attached are joined mechanically but not electrically. All the symbols in Fig. 9-12 show a bar or rectangle at the front depicting that portion of the jack (called the sleeve) which extends out of the chassis, and into which the plug is inserted. This area will sometimes be shown as a heavy solid bar.

The symbols at G and H in Fig. 9-12 are for plugs. The one at G is for a two-conductor plug, and the one at H is for a three-conductor plug.

Like sockets, jacks and plugs are usually not assigned code letters. But if they are, the letter J is the most popular for jacks, and P or PL for plugs, although X and M may sometimes be employed.

PRINTED CIRCUITS

In most types of modern electronic equipment, the wiring has been replaced by a printed circuit. Appropriately named, a printed-circuit board comprises a phenolic base onto which the conductors are "printed" with a conductive pattern. Its biggest advantage is that tedious hand wiring is no longer necessary. Instead, the circuits can be mass produced by machines, a process which is not only quicker but also more reliable. Compactness in equipment design is another virtue of printed circuitry.

The connections made by the printed wiring are shown in exactly the same manner as with hand wiring. If only part of the circuit is printed, that portion may be outlined by a dashed line and identified as such. Ways of identifying the different points of the printed-wiring board will be discussed later.

COMPONENT COMBINATIONS

Two or more components are often contained within a single unit. This is done to save space, cut costs, and prevent interaction between components (thus forestalling a malfunction).

Coil and Transformer Combinations

Various combinations of components are employed. For example, a coil may be wound directly over a resistor, as shown in Fig. 9-13A. Or a capacitor may be connected across one or both windings of a transformer, as shown in Fig. 9-13B. The schematic representations for these two units, as well as other popular combinations, are given in Fig. 9-14. The symbols may be enclosed in a dashed-line box which signifies that all components within it are part of an individual combination unit. Notice the ground symbol connected to the box in C— it indicates that the components within the box are shielded from the rest of the circuit. That is, stray magnetic fields cannot enter or leave the box. This shielding is provided by a metal cover (or *can* as it is more commonly called) which touches the chassis and is thus grounded to it.

Some of the other combinations are also given in Fig. 9-14. The units represented by symbols D, E, F, and G all contain a coil and capacitor. Symbol D has a fixed capacitor connected directly across a coil. In symbol E, the coil is also in parallel but with a variable capacitor. The coils and capacitors in F and G are connected in *series*.

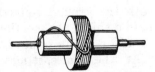

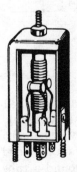

Courtesy Stancor Electronics, Inc.

(A) Resistor and coil.　　　(B) Transformer and capacitors.

Fig. 9-13. Component combinations.

The transformer in symbol H has a resistor connected across one winding and a capacitor across the other. Many other similar combinations are possible. Symbol I represents a transformer, three capacitors, a coil, and a crystal diode—all occupying a single can. Notice that the dashed lines extend all the way around the crystal diode, signifying that the diode itself is entirely enclosed by a separate can. Usually the diode is mounted in two clips on top of the regular can, over which a metal cover is placed to shield the diode.

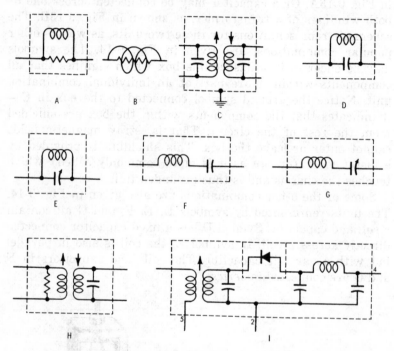

Fig. 9-14. Various coil and transformer combination symbols.

This same dashed-line symbol with the ground connected to it is used in many ways to designate a shield. As mentioned previously, when drawn around a lead or group of leads, it represents a shielded wire or cable. At other times, it may be placed around a tube symbol to denote that a shield is placed over the tube after it has been inserted into its socket.

The various companies differ considerably in the code letters by which the foregoing units are designated. Some assign the same L or T that they do for a regular coil or transformer, but leave the resistors and capacitors unassigned. If more than one coil is included, they are subclassified with an A, B, C, etc. Other companies assign code letters to the individual components just as if they were separate units.

Packaged Electronic Circuits

The units pictured in Fig. 9-15 include several individual components. These devices contain various combinations of resistors, capacitors, and in some instances, coils, all bound to a base plate and sealed with a protective coating. Such units are extremely resistant to moisture, temperature, and shock. Fig. 9-16 should give you an idea of the time and space saved

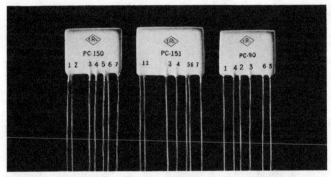

Courtesy Centralab, Electronics Div. of Globe-Union, Inc.

Fig. 9-15. Packaged electronic circuits.

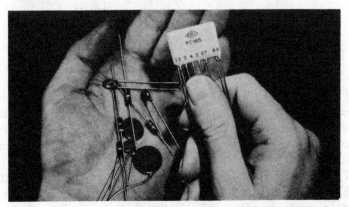

Courtesy Centralab, Electronics Div. of Globe-Union, Inc.

Fig. 9-16. A packaged electronic circuit and the components it replaces.

by using these devices. All the components at the bottom are contained within the single unit at the top. By using this unit, nine soldered connections are eliminated and only one sixth of the space is required. This unit has nine external leads and contains all the components necessary for coupling between two stages of a radio receiver.

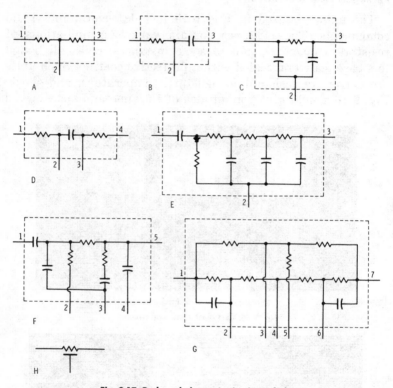

Fig. 9-17. Packaged electronic circuit symbols.

These units are usually represented schematically by using regular resistor and capacitor symbols. The combination is then enclosed within dashed lines to indicate they are contained in a single unit. Each lead is numbered at the point where it extends from the dashed lines.

There are myriad units employing this type of construction. Each will vary only in the number of components, their connection, or their value. Fig. 9-17A through G shows some of the available combinations.

Fig. 9-18. Module from a color-tv receiver.

The dashed lines around the components in the unit are sometimes omitted. Occasionally, the symbol at H in Fig. 9-17 may be used instead of showing the actual internal connections. It may or may not be enclosed within dashed lines.

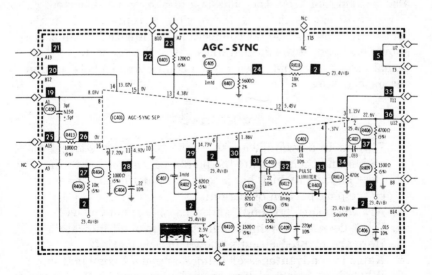

Fig. 9-19. Circuit for the module of Fig. 9-18.

The internal connections are usually shown elsewhere on the schematic.

There are several methods of assigning code letters to these packaged units. Some companies will assign one code letter (*A, E, K, M, N, X, PC, PN, DC,* or *RC*) to the entire unit. Others will assign the letters *R* and *C* to the unit, and designate the individual components as *A, B, C,* etc. Still others may combine the two methods, assigning a code letter and a number to the entire unit and then designating the individual components within it with regular *R* and *C* designations.

Modules

Another method of combining components is shown in Fig. 9-18. This system is very popular in modern television receivers. All the components necessary for a stage in the television receiver are attached to the printed-circuit board. This unit also contains an integrated circuit near the center of the unit. This assembly is then plugged into the main television chassis. Notice the two rows of rectangular holes, some of which have metal inserts at the edge of the board. These are the connectors through which the module is connected to the remainder of the chassis. If a malfunction occurs in this unit, the individual component can be replaced or the entire module can also be removed from the chassis and a new one inserted.

Fig. 9-19 shows the way the module is represented on the schematic. The individual connections within the module are shown enclosed in the dashed lines. Also, the connectors to external circuits are indicated by the connector symbols around the dashed lines.

QUESTIONS

1. Why is it advantageous to show all voltage sources together and then indicate the points which connect to them?
2. Does a symbol which has a solid black dot depict the socket or the plug portion of the unit?
3. Are the terms "ground" and "chassis" synonymous?
4. What does a heavy line connected to ground indicate?
5. How are printed circuits shown in schematics?
6. Name two advantages of using component combinations.
7. What does a dashed line around a component (or group

of components) with a ground symbol connected to it indicate?

8. What does the letter *A* or *B* following the code letter and number of a component usually indicate?
9. Show two methods of illustrating crossing wires which are not connected.
10. Show two ways of depicting an ac line-cord plug.

CHAPTER 10

Combining the Components

In the previous chapters, we have discussed practically every component used in electronic equipment and the methods of connecting them. Also, we have shown how sometimes several components are combined in a single unit. However, before any of these components can serve a useful purpose, they must be connected to form a circuit.

What is a circuit? A circuit is any combination of components connected in such a manner that it will perform its intended function.

A passive circuit is one which does not contain a tube or transistor; that is, it is merely a combination of resistors, capacitors, and coils. In certain applications, such a circuit can perform many useful functions. For example, frequencies below a certain point will pass through the circuit in Fig. 10-1A and on to the following circuit. Above a certain frequency, the signals are shunted (bypassed) to ground by the capacitors. The opposite is true of the circuit in Fig. 10-1B. This is a high-pass filter. Below a certain frequency, the signals are shunted to ground through the coils; above this frequency, they are passed on to the next stage.

There are many passive circuits, or configurations as they are sometimes called, like the ones in Fig. 10-1. Each performs a definite purpose in the overall operation of the unit.

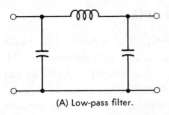
(A) Low-pass filter.

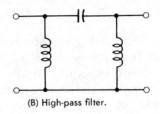
(B) High-pass filter.

Fig. 10-1. Two passive circuits.

RECTIFIER CIRCUITS

Perhaps the simplest circuit is the rectifier shown in Fig. 10-2. Recall that in order for a diode to conduct, the anode must be more positive than the cathode. Then electrons will flow from the cathode to the anode. The anode is connected to an alternating voltage. Hence, during the periods when the anode is positive, electrons will flow from the cathode to the anode. However, these electrons must come from somewhere. They flow from ground up through R3, then through R2 to the cathode. Since electrons flowing through a resistor produce a voltage drop across it, a voltage (which will be positive at the top) will be produced across R3. This voltage will also be present on capacitors C1 and C2.

During the period when the alternating voltage on the anode is negative, the tube will not conduct. But since the primary purpose of a capacitor is to store electrons, it will hold the charge previously placed on it and maintain the voltage relatively constant. Thus, while ac is applied to the anode, the current through R3, R2, CR1, and R1 is dc. This is the purpose of the rectifier—the ac has been converted to dc. The voltage at the output of the rectifier, called the B+ voltage, is used to power the tubes or transistors in the unit. This circuit will operate in the same way if a diode-tube rectifier is used in place of the semiconductor rectifier in Fig. 10-2.

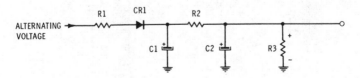

Fig. 10-2. A typical rectifier circuit.

Fig. 10-3 shows the basic triode amplifier circuit. The plate of the tube is connected (through resistor R2) to the dc B+ voltage explained in the foregoing. The signal, which is ac, is applied to the left plate of capacitor C1. Since an ac signal will, in effect, pass through the capacitor, it also appears at the grid of the tube. As explained in Chapter 5, this signal will be amplified by the tube and appear at the plate. Here, capacitor C2 couples the amplified signal on to the next tube (or stage as it is called in electronics terminology).

The circuit in Fig. 10-3 is called a resistance-capacitance–coupled (RC) circuit. A transformer-coupled circuit is given

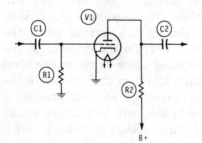

Fig. 10-3. An RC-coupled, grounded-cathode amplifier circuit.

in Fig. 10-4. Its operation is similar to that of the circuit in Fig. 10-3. The transformer secondary and C1 are tuned so that only a narrow band of frequencies will pass. Therefore, only the desired frequencies are coupled to the grid of the tube. The amplified signal appears at the plate and is coupled via T2 (which is tuned by C2 to the desired frequency) to the next stage.

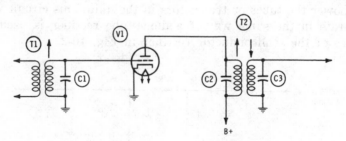

Fig. 10-4. A transformer-coupled amplifier circuit.

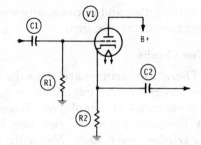

Fig. 10-5. A cathode-follower circuit.

Another type of circuit is given in Fig. 10-5. Here the signal is coupled to the grid of the tube via C1—the same as in Fig. 10-3. However, here the similarity ends. Notice that the plate is connected directly to the B+ voltage source, so the signal will be bypassed to ground by the filter capacitors in the power supply. Also notice R2 and C2 connected to the cathode. In this circuit, called a *cathode follower,* the signal is developed across resistor R2 and coupled to the next stage by C2. No gain is accomplished in this circuit; in fact, there will be a slight loss. But, in certain applications the cathode follower has advantages over the amplifier circuit of Fig. 10-4.

Still another version of the triode amplifier is given in Fig. 10-6. This is called a *grounded-grid* amplifier. The signal is applied to the cathode, and the output is at the plate in this circuit. As you can see, the grid is not actually connected to ground as implied by the name. However, capacitor C1, connected between the grid and ground, serves as a by-

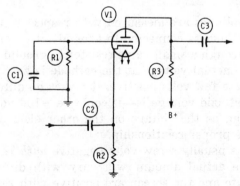

Fig. 10-6. A grounded-grid amplifier circuit.

pass capacitor and removes any variations in the voltage which might occur at the grid.

Other Circuits

There are many variations in the basic circuits given in the foregoing. As explained in Chapter 5, often tetrode or pentode tubes are employed. Except for the added components for the screen circuit, operation is basically the same as for the triodes given here. Normally the signal is applied to the grid. The changes in the grid voltage caused by this signal increase or decrease the number of electrons which can flow through the tube from cathode to plate. Thus, the number of electrons flowing out the plate and through the plate load (i.e., the resistor or transformer winding connected to the plate) varies in step with the signal on the grid. This varying electron flow produces a varying drop across the plate load, and this drop is coupled to the next stage. Since a small change at the grid produces a much larger change at the plate, the signal is said to be amplified.

The foregoing is true no matter whether a triode, tetrode, or pentode tube is used. There are many special circuits which will generate their own signal, change the form of the applied signal, and perform many other functions. How these circuits operate is beyond the scope of this book. Suffice it to say that the same basic idea of electrons flowing from cathode to plate, and the amount of this flow being affected by the elements between the cathode and plate, still applies.

Tube Voltages

All tube voltages are measured with respect to the cathode. Often the cathode is connected to ground; at other times it is connected through a small-value resistor to ground. In the first instance, the actual voltage at the cathode is zero; in the latter, it will be a few volts positive. It makes no difference what the actual cathode voltage is—it could be −100 volts or +100 volts—as long as the voltage on the other elements is maintained in the proper relationship.

The grid is usually a few volts negative *with respect to the cathode*. The actual amount will vary with different tubes. Both the plate and the screen are positive with respect to the cathode. Normally this difference will be from 100 to 200 volts, but sometimes it is less and sometimes more. Usually the plate will be slightly more positive than the screen grid, but sometimes the two voltages will be the same, and in certain instances, the screen will be more positive than the plate. The suppressor grid is usually connected to ground or to the cathode; hence, at most there will be only a few volts difference between it and the cathode.

BASIC BIPOLAR TRANSISTOR CIRCUITS

Like tubes, transistors can be connected in three different ways—the common emitter, common base, and common collector. Also, since both pnp and npn transistors are used, the number of variations is doubled. Now let's look at each of the basic transistor circuits and see how it operates.

The Common-Emitter Circuit

A common-emitter circuit using a pnp transistor is given in Fig. 10-7A, while the same circuit with an npn transistor is given in Fig. 10-7B. Like its vacuum-tube counterpart—the grounded-cathode amplifier—the common-emitter circuit is the most popular. First look at Fig. 10-7A. The signal is coupled via C1 to the base of transistor Q1. R1 and R2 establish the proper operating voltages on the base, and R3 establishes the operating voltage on the emitter. The amplified

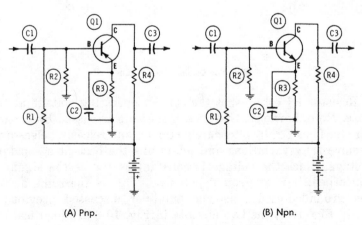

(A) Pnp.   (B) Npn.

Fig. 10-7. Common-emitter circuits.

signal appears across R4 and is coupled to the next stage via C3.

The circuit in Fig. 10-7B is the npn version of the same circuit. Again, the signal is coupled to the transistor via C1, and the amplified version of the signal appears across R4 and is coupled via C3 to the next stage.

The only difference between the two circuits in Fig. 10-7 is the type of transistor and the way the battery is connected in the circuit. (The operating voltages will be discussed later.)

The Common-Base Circuit

The two circuits in Fig. 10-8 show the pnp and npn versions of the common-base circuit. The input signal is coupled to the emitter of the transistor via C1. The amplified signal appears across R3 and at the collector of the transistor. Here it is coupled to the next stage via C3.

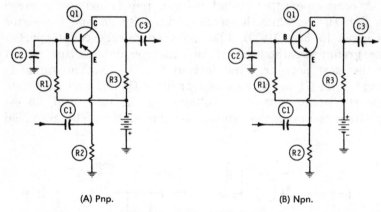

(A) Pnp.   (B) Npn.

Fig. 10-8. Common-base circuits.

Resistor R1 establishes the correct operating voltage at the base. Note, however, that this resistor is bypassed by capacitor C2. Thus C2, by alternately storing and releasing electrons, removes any variations and maintains the base at a constant voltage. Since the voltage is constant as far as the signal is concerned, it is at ground potential. This is the same as for the grounded-grid tube-type amplifier discussed previously. As in Fig. 10-7, the two circuits in Fig. 10-8 are identical except for the type of transistor and the polarity of the battery.

The Common-Collector Circuit

The pnp and the npn versions of the common-collector circuit are given in Fig. 10-9. The input signal is coupled by C1 to the base of transistor Q1, and the output signal appears across emitter resistor R3. Then it is coupled via C3 to the following stage. Resistors R1 and R2 establish the proper operating voltage at the base of the transistor. R4 performs the same function at the collector but, like the base of the previous circuit, the collector is bypassed by a capacitor (C2). Hence, as far as the signal is concerned, the collector is at ground potential. Again, the only difference in the two circuits are the transistor type and the polarity of the battery.

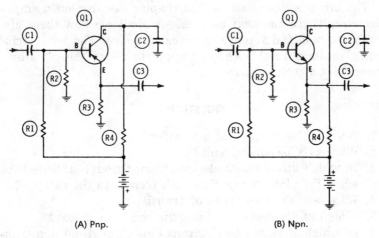

(A) Pnp. (B) Npn.

Fig. 10-9. Common-collector circuits.

Voltages

As we have pointed out in each of the basic circuits, the negative terminal of the battery is connected (through a resistor) to the collector of a pnp transistor, while for the npn transistor the battery is reversed. Unlike a tube, in which electrons always flow in one direction (from cathode to plate), the electron flow through the two types of transistors is in opposite directions.

Electrons always flow from the negative terminal of a battery, through the circuit, to the positive terminal. In a pnp transistor electrons flow from collector to emitter; hence, the collector must be the most negative point. The base is maintained a few tenths of a volt negative with respect to the emitter. Therefore, the emitter has the most positive voltage of any of the elements.

The opposite is true of the npn transistor. Here, the electrons must flow from the emitter to the collector. Therefore, the emitter is the most negative point. The base is a few tenths of a volt positive with respect to the emitter, and the collector is the most positive point.

SUMMARY

The circuits discussed in this chapter are the *basic* amplifier circuits. In the next chapter, we shall see how these circuits are modified for use in actual practice. The basic principles outlined in this chapter apply to all of the circuits—regardless of the refinements.

QUESTIONS

1. What is the purpose of a rectifier?
2. What is a passive circuit?
3. In which direction do electrons flow through a diode tube when the plate is negative with respect to the cathode?
4. What are the two types of transistors?
5. Which of the basic tube circuits produces a loss?
6. In which direction do electrons flow through an npn transistor?
7. What element of the tube is used as the reference point for all tube voltages?
8. What are the three basic transistor circuits?
9. What are the three basic tube circuits?
10. From what terminal of a battery do electrons flow?

CHAPTER 11

Reading and Interpreting Schematic Diagrams

Most schematics follow the same general arrangement. The input is normally at the upper left-hand corner, and from here, the path is usually arranged in rows from left to right and from top to bottom. Starting at the input, you can trace your way through the individual circuits as if you were reading a book. The best way to read a schematic is to analyze each stage, forming a mental image of what happens in it, and then see where its output goes. This is the input of the next "block" in the equipment. Continue through all the stages until you reach the output device (i.e., speaker, picture tube, indicator, etc.).

If this pattern is followed for any schematic, the operation of any equipment—whether it be a radio or TV receiver, transmitter, radar, or even a computer—should become apparent.

RADIO-RECEIVER SCHEMATIC ANALYSIS

The schematic of a typical five-transistor radio receiver is given in Fig. 11-1. Let's see just what information it contains.

The Signal Path

It is suggested that you refer to Fig. 11-1 as we follow the signal from transistor to transistor (stage to stage in electron-

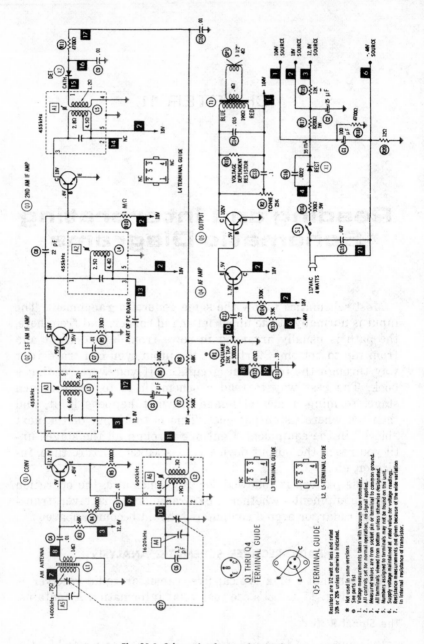

Fig. 11-1. Schematic of a transistor radio.

ics terminology) on its journey through the radio. The same general principles can then be applied to many other circuits.

The Converter—The first stage (transistor) in most present-day radios is the converter, which actually functions as an rf amplifier, oscillator, and mixer. The signal is first intercepted by loop antenna L1 in Fig. 11-1. The two variable capacitors connected across L1 tune the circuit to the frequency of the desired station. The signal is then connected to the base of converter transistor Q1. Coil L2, the two variable capacitors, fixed capacitors C5 and C6 and a portion of Q1 form the oscillator portion of the stage.

The signal from the oscillator and the one from the antenna are combined, or mixed, within the transistor. The two original signals are still present at the output (collector) of the transistor, but two more also appear. One is equal to the sum of the frequencies of the two original signals, and the other is equal to the difference between them. Both are exactly like the original antenna signal except in frequency. Transformer L3 is "tuned" to accept this difference frequency, called the i-f (intermediate frequency) and to pass it across the secondary to the next stage.

I-F Amplifier—The next stage is the i-f (intermediate-frequency) amplifier. The i-f signal at the secondary of transformer L3 is connected to the base of i-f amplifier Q2. Here the signal will be boosted, or amplified, by the time it reaches the collector. The collector circuit of transistor Q2 is tuned by coil L4 and the capacitor connected across it so that the correct band of frequencies (455 kHz, the i-f frequency) will be the most prominent. The i-f frequencies are then coupled to the second base of the second i-f amplifier transistor (Q3) by capacitor C8. The signal is further amplified by Q3 and appears at the collector of this transistor and across the primary of transformer L5. Normal transformer action couples the signal to the secondary of L5 for application to the next stage.

Detector, AVC, and Audio Amplifier—The signal from L5 is connected to signal diode X2 where it undergoes a change by a process called detection. Here the carrier signal from the transmitter is removed and a signal which corresponds to the original one—music, speech, etc.—at the station appears across volume control R1. This is the audio-frequency signal (one whose frequency can be heard by the human ear). It is far too feeble to operate a speaker (although it could be heard from an earphone connected at this point).

A portion (the amount depends on the volume control setting) of this audio signal is coupled to the base of Q4 through the .22-μF capacitor (C12). Here, it is amplified by the transistor and appears at the collector.

Another voltage is also developed, by resistors R6, R7, and R8, and C3. Called the avc (automatic volume control) voltage, it varies according to the strength of the signal received at the antenna. It is applied through L3 to the base of Q2 to change the gain, or amount of amplification. Thus, if the signal becomes stronger or weaker (say, because of atmospheric conditions), the gain of the previous stages is automatically decreased or increased accordingly, to compensate for the change.

Audio-Output Stage—The signal at the collector of Q4 is directly coupled to the base of audio output transistor Q5. Like the other stages, it amplifies the signal which then appears at the collector and across transformer T1. The speaker (SP1) connected across the secondary of T1 converts the amplified signal into sound.

Power Supply—Before any of the stages discussed in the foregoing can work, the proper voltages must be applied to them. This is the purpose of the components located in the lower-right corner of the schematic (Fig. 11-1). The line cord, which is plugged into a 117-volt ac outlet, is shown at the left. The next symbol is the on-off switch S1; it connects one side of the line to the rectifier (X1).

Rf bypass capacitors C15 and C16 remove any high-frequency noise that might be present on the power lines and be passed into the receiver. R16 serves as a fuse and also helps smooth out any surges on the ac power line.

You will recall from the previous chapter that a diode will conduct only when its anode is more positive than its cathode. The ac line voltage varies from positive to negative; hence, during the positive half-cycles the diode conducts and a pulsating dc is present at the cathode. The two electrolytic capacitors (C1 and C2) and resistor R17 smooth out these pulsations. Thus the voltage at the output is essentially dc.

At the output of the rectifier in Fig. 11-1, 104 volts is present. This is labeled as the "104V Source" on the schematic.

However, most of the transistors in this receiver do not require such a high voltage. R17 and R19 in Fig. 11-1 drop this voltage to the 18 and 12.8 volts for operation of the other transistors. Notice C1 is not connected directly to ground, but that a 12-ohm resistor is connected between the negative side of the capacitor and ground. This is a special arrangement that provides the −.44-volt source. Thus many arrangements of resistors and capacitors can be included in the power supply to provide the proper voltage for operation of the various stages.

Voltage and Current

In addition to the signal path, many more items are included on the schematic diagram. One is the voltage at each element of every transistor. This information comes in handy for troubleshooting the equipment. Also included in the power supply section is the total current flowing through the rectifier (36 mA, for milliamperes). The power rating of the equipment (4 watts at 117 volts) is given at the line cord. The notes at the lower left state the conditions under which the voltage measurements were taken.

Other Information on Schematics

Many other items are included in Fig. 11-1, and each is useful in analyzing circuit operation or in troubleshooting. For example, drawings show the location of the terminals on the coil. These numbers are also included on the schematic symbols. While these numbers may not actually appear on the transformers, they will aid you in locating the various points. Other drawings show the basing of the transistors.

Transformers and other components often have colored leads for identification. These are shown in Fig. 11-1 for audio-output transformer T1. Also given beside each coil on the schematic is its resistance, since the easiest method of checking the condition of a coil is to measure its resistance.

Letter-and-number combinations A1 through A6, shown in the squares, are the alignment points for the receiver. Adjustments are made here, according to the instructions, to tune each stage to the proper frequency.

The numbers 1 through 21 in the black boxes appear on the schematic and also in Fig. 11-2, a photograph of the chassis.

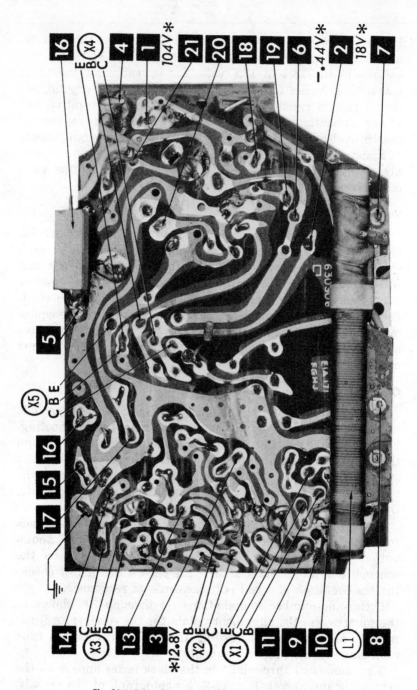

Fig. 11-2. Printed circuit used in the radio of Fig. 11-1.

164

Called CIRCUITRACE (a tradename of Howard W. Sams & Co., Inc.), this system greatly aids in locating the various points on a printed-circuit board. By referring to the schematic and Fig. 11-2 simultaneously, technicians are saved tedious tracing of the printed wiring.

TUBE-TYPE RECEIVER

Although not as common today as in the past, the schematic of a tube-type ac/dc radio is presented in Fig. 11-3, to show how such a circuit operates. By following the signal through the circuit, stage-by-stage, it will be seen it is much like the transistor radio discussed previously.

The signal from the various stations are received at the loop antenna L1. The two variable capacitors, with the coil, "tune" the circuit to the desired signal, which is applied to one of the grids (pin 7) of the converter tube (V1). Coil L2, the two variable capacitors, fixed capacitor C5, resistor R2, the grid (pin 1) and cathode (pin 2) form the oscillator circuit. The grid (pin 6) of the tube functions much as the plate for the oscillator portion. Both the signals, plus their sum and difference signals will appear at the plate (pin 5) of the tube, just as they did for the transistor stage. The i-f transformer L3 is tuned to the difference frequency and couples it to the i-f amplifier tube (V2). Here it is amplified and appears at the plate of the tube and is coupled by L4 to the next stage.

The signal from L5 is connected to pin 5 of dual-purpose tube V3. This element is a diode plate and with the cathode (pin 2) functions the same as any other diode tube. Thus, this is the detector portion of the tube. The detected audio signal will appear across the volume control (with S1A in radio position). A portion of this signal is coupled via the .005 capacitor in component combination PC1 to the grid (pin 1) of V3. (Pins 1, 2, and 7 of V3 form a triode tube.) Here, the signal is amplified and appears at the plate. Then it is coupled to the grid of V4, via component combination PC1. V4, a beam-power amplifier tube, further amplifies the audio signal, which is then transformer coupled to the speaker.

The power supply is at the lower right in Fig. 11-3. The line cord is shown at the left. The next symbol is for an ac interlock, a special type of plug and socket arrangement that re-

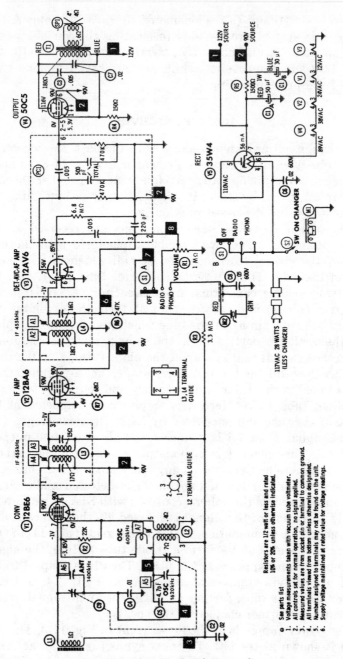

Fig. 11-3. Schematic of a tube-type radio.

moves the line voltage from the receiver when the back is removed. When switch S1B is moved to the radio position, one side of the ac line is connected to the tube. The tap on the rectifier tube filament is to allow a dial light to be connected across pins 6 and 4. The voltage drop across these pins is 6.3 volts—the proper amount to operate a dial lamp. No dial light is used in this receiver, so it is not shown. The ac line voltage (minus the 6.3-volt drop) will then be applied to the plate (pin 5) of the tube. Thus, whenever the cathode is made negative by the ac power line, the tube will conduct and normal rectifier action will occur. C1A, C1B, and R5 form the filtering circuit to smooth the pulsating dc to the steady dc needed for proper operation of the tubes.

The symbols extending in a row from pin 3 of V5 represent the filaments of the other tubes in the radio. This arrangement is called a series string. If the voltages of all the tubes are added up, they equal the line voltage, so no transformer is needed to obtain the lower ac voltage needed to heat the tubes. The disadvantage of such an arrangement is that if the filament of one of the tubes opens, all will cease to operate.

In addition to the radio, the unit in Fig. 11-3 also includes a phonograph. Notice, in either the radio or phono position the shorting bar on S1B will connect ac power to the rectifier tube. Closing switch S2 will cause power also to be applied to the phono motor (M1). Switch S1 is a two-section switch; the other portion is located directly below V3. In the radio position, the output of the detector is connected to the volume control through the switch. In the phono position, the converter, i-f amplifier, and the detector are disconnected and the phono cartridge (M2) is connected to the volume control. C8 is an rf bypass capacitor.

As for the transistor receiver of Fig. 11-1, many other items are included in Fig. 11-3. Colors of various leads, voltages, pin numbers of the various tubes, and many other items designed to aid in servicing the receiver are included.

FROM SCHEMATIC TO CHASSIS

One of the most difficult problems a beginner faces is to locate, on the chassis, a component included in a schematic; or to look at a schematic and construct the circuit. Unfortunately, as you saw in Chapter 1, the actual chassis does not look like the schematic. In fact, in the schematic a resistor may be shown next to a tube element, but may be at the other side of the chassis. The reason is that a schematic can show electrical connections only, but a component must also have some means of mechanical support.

Terminal strips are often included on the chassis, and the terminals utilized for connecting between two points. Not all pins are used for internal connections on all tubes, but the tube socket will have terminals for each pin. For example, for mechanical support, one end of the resistor may be connected to an unused tube-socket terminal, which is then connected by a wire at the other end of the circuit. With printed circuits, often the printed wiring must be arranged in a certain manner to make all the connections.

If you have a photograph like the ones shown in Chapter 1 or Fig. 11-2, a component is easy to locate. But the component can still be located, even if only the schematic is available. Just look for a familiar nearby point in the circuit. (Tube, pins or transistor leads are usually the most convenient points.) Then see what components are connected between this point and the desired component. Next find this point on the schematic, and follow any wire or printed-circuit pattern connected to it. Be sure to trace out all leads connected to any tie points (terminal strips or unused tube pins). If you encounter a component not connected between the wanted one and the starting point, go back and try a different route. While such hit-and-miss tracing sounds tedious, with a little practice it soon becomes easy and fast. Remember: the fact that a component is connected to a tube-socket terminal doesn't mean there is an internal connection to the tube. This connection may be there for mechanical support only.

OTHER TYPES OF EQUIPMENT

No matter how complex, the schematic of any piece of electronic equipment can be broken down into individual stages, as you did in the first of this chapter. Then by following the connections between stages you will be able to fit the blocks together and in this way determine the overall operation of the circuit.

QUESTIONS

1. Where is the input normally located on a schematic?
2. What three functions are performed by the converter stage?
3. What additional aid in locating transformer leads is often included on a schematic?
4. What is the purpose of the avc voltage?
5. How does the i-f signal differ from the signal received from the station?
6. What is the best way to analyze a schematic?
7. What type of signal appears across the volume control?
8. What is the disadvantage of connecting all tube filaments in series?
9. Does an earphone or a speaker require more power for operation?
10. What is the purpose of an rf bypass capacitor?

CHAPTER 12

Logic Symbols

Many times, the actual circuit components—and the manner in which they are connected—are not of prime interest. For example, the actual circuit components within an integrated circuit, such as was shown in Fig. 6-22 are seldom of interest. If a circuit to perform the same function were to be constructed using individual components (called discrete components), the choice of components and connections would probably be different anyway.

A diagram such as that shown in Fig. 12-1A is often used for integrated circuits. Here, each of the four symbols inside the box represent the components shown in the schematic of Fig. 12-1B. Thus, this IC contains the equivalent of 16 transistors, 12 diodes, and 28 resistors—making it a relatively simple integrated circuit. The symbols within the box of Fig. 12-1A are called logic symbols. In the remainder of this chapter, some of these symbols, and their use in digital circuits will be explained.

DIGITAL CIRCUITS

In digital electronics instead of having a continuously variable quantity such as the signals that have been shown in the previous chapters of this book (called analog signals), the output varies in discrete steps. That is, a digital signal will consist of a series of pulses or an on-off operation. Thus, an analog device involves directly measurable quantities such as voltage, resistance, current, etc., while digital devices count like an adding machine. By coding the pulses, various quantities—numbers, letters, etc.—can be represented.

Digital computers are the most familiar application of digital electronics. However, there are many more. Modern television receivers often employ digital circuits. The same principles are used in the control circuits of many electronic devices. Relays, transistors, ICs, and other control devices can all be better understood through logic.

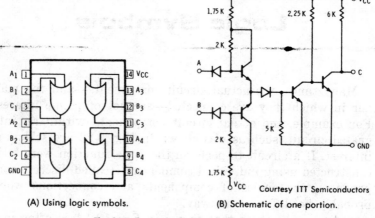

(A) Using logic symbols.   (B) Schematic of one portion.

Courtesy ITT Semiconductors

Fig. 12-1. An integrated circuit diagram.

The simplest logic element is an on-off switch. It has two positions—on and off—which can represent the two states of digital electronics. By letting the open position of the switch represent 0 and the closed position a 1, we have the two digits of the binary numbering system. By various combinations of switches, more complex functions can be represented. These circuits are called *gates* because they are used to block or pass an electronic current. In usage, instead of an on-off condition, a high and a low level of a continuous signal may represent the two conditions. While switches are used to represent the various gates in the following discussions, in actual practice, a transistor, diode, or similar device can be made to conduct or block a signal flow. Thus, the transistor, diode, etc., forms an electronic switch.

AND GATE

The AND gate can be represented by the two switches connected as shown in Fig. 12-2A. Here, if either switch is open, there is no complete path for current. However, if both switch A *and* B are closed, there will be a complete circuit and an output will be present. More switches could be added in the series, and all would have to be closed before there is a complete path for current. These switches represent the various inputs of the logic circuit. Thus in an AND gate, there must be a pulse to all inputs to obtain an output.

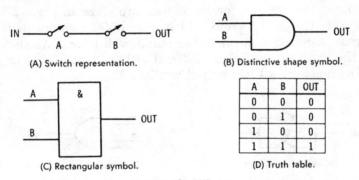

(A) Switch representation.

(B) Distinctive shape symbol.

(C) Rectangular symbol.

(D) Truth table.

A	B	OUT
0	0	0
0	1	0
1	0	0
1	1	1

Fig. 12-2. The AND gate.

The AND gate is usually represented by the symbol in Fig. 12-2B. The two lines extending from the left labeled A and B are the inputs. (The A and B in Fig. 12-2B are not part of the symbol but placed here and on subsequent symbols for identification only.) Thus, if there is an input at both A and B there will be an output. However, if either input is missing, there will be no output. Another type symbol is shown in Fig. 12-2C. In this system a rectangular or square box is used to represent all types of logic devices. Then a qualifying symbol (letter or other character) is added to the box to indicate the type of gate. Here the & signifies an AND gate.

The means of showing the various input and output conditions in a logic circuit is given in Fig. 12-2D. This device, called a *truth table,* provides a means to quickly determine the operation of the circuit. In the truth table, a *0* represents open position and *1* represents the closed position (or *0* is the no signal and *1* is the signal condition). Referring to Fig. 12-2D, it can be seen that if A and B or either A or B is 0, the output is 0, and if both A *and* B are 1s, the output is a 1. Thus, the name AND gate signifies that all inputs—A *and* B *and* C, etc.—must be present for an output.

OR GATE

If two switches are connected as shown in Fig. 12-3A, you will notice that if either switch A *or* B is closed, there will be an output. Thus, this is the representation of an OR gate. Just as for the basic AND gate, more switches can be added to the OR gate. The symbols for an OR gate are given in Fig. 12-3B and Fig. 12-3C. The symbol $\geqq 1$ in Fig. 12-3C signifies that if one or more inputs are a 1, the output will be a 1. As shown in the truth table of Fig. 12-3D, if either input is a 1, or if both inputs are a 1, the output will be a 1.

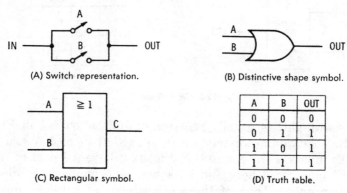

(A) Switch representation.

(B) Distinctive shape symbol.

(C) Rectangular symbol.

A	B	OUT
0	0	0
0	1	1
1	0	1
1	1	1

(D) Truth table.

Fig. 12-3. The OR gate.

NAND GATE

In logic terminology, *not* signifies the negation or reverse of a condition. For example, if one position of a two-position switch is designated A, the other position is not-A (written as $\bar{A}$ or A^1). An inverter reverses the normal operation of a circuit. Therefore, if we combine an inverter, which is simply a low-gain amplifier with the AND circuit of Fig. 12-2, we have a *not-and* circuit, called a NAND circuit. Figs. 12-4A and B show the symbols for a NAND circuit. In both symbols the circle combined with the AND symbol signifies the negation or

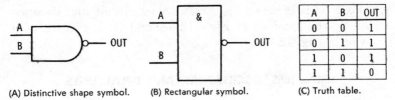

A	B	OUT
0	0	1
0	1	1
1	0	1
1	1	0

(A) Distinctive shape symbol.   (B) Rectangular symbol.   (C) Truth table.

Fig. 12-4. The NAND gate.

inverting function. The truth table in Fig. 12-4C shows the reverse of the AND circuit. That is, if either or both of the inputs is a 0 the output will be a 1 and if both inputs are 1, the output will be a 0.

NOR GATE

By combining the not function with the OR gate, we obtain a *not-or* or NOR gate. As you no doubt have guessed by now, with a NOR gate, if one or more of the inputs are a 1, the output will be 0. Figs. 12-5A and B show the symbols for the NOR gate. As for the NAND gate, the circle added to the OR-gate symbol shows the inverting function. The truth table is given in Fig. 12-5C.

EXCLUSIVE OR GATE

Sometimes, a circuit is needed in which a current will pass if one switch or the other is activated, but not when both are

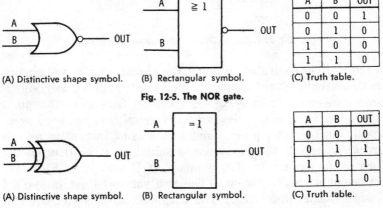

A	B	OUT
0	0	1
0	1	0
1	0	0
1	1	0

(A) Distinctive shape symbol.   (B) Rectangular symbol.   (C) Truth table.

Fig. 12-5. The NOR gate.

A	B	OUT
0	0	0
0	1	1
1	0	1
1	1	0

(A) Distinctive shape symbol.   (B) Rectangular symbol.   (C) Truth table.

Fig. 12-6. The exclusive OR gate.

175

activated. This is called an *exclusive* OR circuit and is represented by the symbols in Figs. 12-6A and B. The truth table is given in Fig. 12-6C.

AMPLIFIERS, OSCILLATORS, AND DELAY LINES

As mentioned previously, amplifiers are employed in logic circuits. The symbols at A and B in Fig. 12-7 shows the methods of designating amplifiers in the two systems of drawing logic diagrams. The symbols at A and B represent a noninverting amplifier. That is the output will be a 1 only if the input is a 1. The symbols at C and D in Fig. 12-7 are for an inverter (also called a *negator*). Again, the circle signifies the inverting (NOT) function. With these, the output will be the 0 state only if the input is the 1 state.

The symbols at E and F in Fig. 12-7 represent an oscillator. The output of this device is a uniform repetitive signal which alternates between the 0 state and the 1 state. (The "G" in the rectangular symbol stands for generator.)

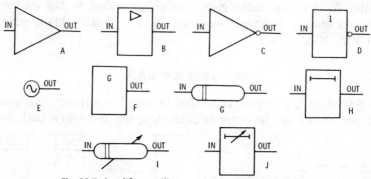

Fig. 12-7. Amplifier, oscillator, and delay element symbols.

Often it is desirable to delay the signal at a certain point in the circuit. Such delays are necessary because any signal processing requires a certain amount of time even though it is minute. Thus, if it is desired for a signal that has been processed to arrive at a given point at the same instant as an unprocessed signal the unprocessed signal must be delayed before being passed on. The symbols at G and H in Fig. 12-7 represent a delay element. (The two vertical lines in symbol G signify the input side.) The output from this element will assume its 1 state only after a specified period of time following the transition of the input to the 1 state, and the output reverts to the 0 state only after the specific period of time following the reverting of the input to the 0 state. The amount of time delay is usually indicated on the symbol. Delay elements can also be made adjustable. In this case, an arrow is added as shown at I and J in Fig. 12-7.

OTHER LOGIC SYMBOLS

Other logic symbols will be encountered but the ones given in this chapter cover all the basic applications. Remember, while only two inputs were shown for the gates in this chapter, any number may be used. The symbols at A and B in Fig. 12-8 show how the lines are extended for the distinctive shape AND and OR gates to accommodate more inputs. The shape of the rectangular symbol is altered instead of using the extension if space does not allow all the inputs.

The symbol at C may be used to represent the AND circuit; the symbol at D may be used to represent the OR circuit; and the symbol at E may be used to represent the inverter (not) function. The use of the symbols at C, D, and E is not recommended, however.

In logic statments, the plus sign (+) represents the OR junction. Thus, in this application, it does not mean add but logical OR. A dot (·), parentheses (), or the absence of a sign signifies logical AND. As mentioned previously, a line over a letter (Ā) signifies the inversion or not function.

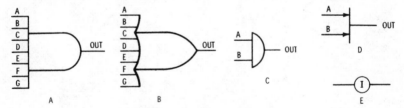

Fig. 12-8. Other logic symbols.

REVIEW QUESTIONS

1. What is an analog circuit?
2. What is a digital circuit?

3. What is another name for a digital switch?
4. Draw the symbol for an AND gate.
5. Draw the symbol for an OR gate.
6. What does the + sign indicate in logic usage?

7. What does this symbol represent? ⟩⟩ ⟩—

8. What does this symbol represent? —◁▯ ⟩—
9. Draw the symbol for an inverting amplifier.
10. Draw the symbol for a NAND gate.

APPENDIX A

House Wiring Symbols

───── CIRCUITS ─────

────────────── Branch Circuits, Concealed in Ceiling or Wall

Without further designation, symbols at left indicate 2-wire. For other designate as follows:

── ── ── Branch Circuits, Concealed in Floor

───── /// ──── (3 wire)

- - - - - - - - Branch Circuits, Exposed

───── // ── // ── (4 wire) etc.

──────► Home Run to Panel Board (Number of Arrowheads Indicates Number of Circuits.)

────────── Feeder

───── GENERAL OUTLETS ─────

Ceiling	Wall		Ceiling	Wall	
◯	—◯	Outlet	Ⓡ	—Ⓡ	Recessed Incandescent Outlet
Ⓑ	—Ⓑ	Blanked Outlet	Ⓥ	—Ⓥ	Vapor Discharge Lamp Outlet
Ⓒ	—Ⓒ	Clock Outlet	Ⓧ	—Ⓧ	Exit Light
Ⓓ		Drop Cord	⦀◯	—⦀◯	Night Light
Ⓕ	—Ⓕ	Fan Outlet	**Ceiling**	**Wall**	
Ⓗ	—Ⓗ	Unit Heater or Cooler Outlet	▭◯▭ —▭◯▭ Fluorescent Fixture Outlet (Surface or Pendent)		
Ⓙ	—Ⓙ	Junction Box	▭◯R▭ —▭◯R▭ Fluorescent Fixture Outlet (Recessed)		
Ⓛ	—Ⓛ	Lampholder	▭◯▭▭ Continuous Row Fluorescent		
Ⓛ PS	—Ⓛ PS	Lampholder with Pull Switch	▭◯R▭▭ Continuous Row Fluorescent (Recessed)		

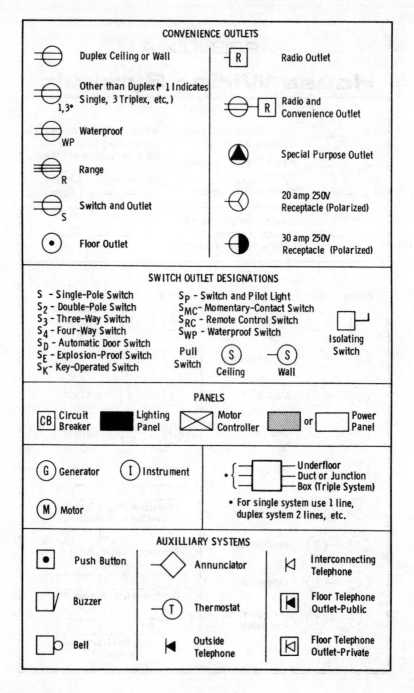

CONVENIENCE OUTLETS

Duplex Ceiling or Wall

Other than Duplex (* 1 Indicates Single, 3 Triplex, etc.)

Waterproof

Range

Switch and Outlet

Floor Outlet

Radio Outlet

Radio and Convenience Outlet

Special Purpose Outlet

20 amp 250V Receptacle (Polarized)

30 amp 250V Receptacle (Polarized)

SWITCH OUTLET DESIGNATIONS

S – Single-Pole Switch
S_2 – Double-Pole Switch
S_3 – Three-Way Switch
S_4 – Four-Way Switch
S_D – Automatic Door Switch
S_E – Explosion-Proof Switch
S_K – Key-Operated Switch

S_P – Switch and Pilot Light
S_{MC} – Momentary-Contact Switch
S_{RC} – Remote Control Switch
S_{WP} – Waterproof Switch

Pull Switch

Ceiling

Wall

Isolating Switch

PANELS

Circuit Breaker

Lighting Panel

Motor Controller

or

Power Panel

Generator   Instrument

Motor

Underfloor Duct or Junction Box (Triple System)

• For single system use 1 line, duplex system 2 lines, etc.

AUXILLIARY SYSTEMS

Push Button

Buzzer

Bell

Annunciator

Thermostat

Outside Telephone

Interconnecting Telephone

Floor Telephone Outlet-Public

Floor Telephone Outlet-Private

APPENDIX B

Appliance Symbols

Many of the same symbols described previously are also used in the appliance industry. However, there are some differences, and some additional components are also used. These symbols are shown in the following chart.

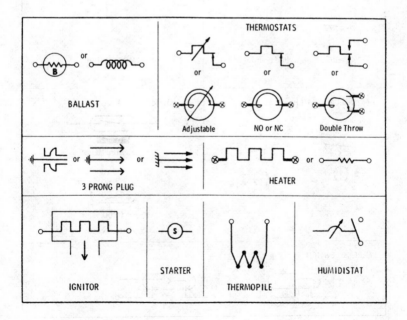

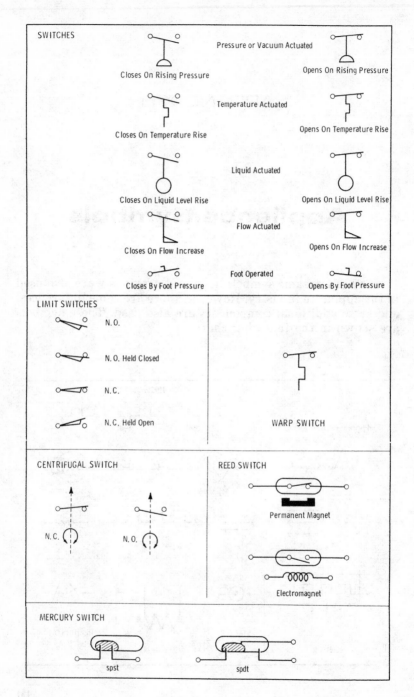

SWITCHES

Pressure or Vacuum Actuated

Closes On Rising Pressure   Opens On Rising Pressure

Temperature Actuated

Closes On Temperature Rise   Opens On Temperature Rise

Liquid Actuated

Closes On Liquid Level Rise   Opens On Liquid Level Rise

Flow Actuated

Closes On Flow Increase   Opens On Flow Increase

Foot Operated

Closes By Foot Pressure   Opens By Foot Pressure

LIMIT SWITCHES

N.O.

N.O. Held Closed

N.C.

N.C. Held Open

WARP SWITCH

CENTRIFUGAL SWITCH

N.C.   N.O.

REED SWITCH

Permanent Magnet

Electromagnet

MERCURY SWITCH

spst   spdt

APPENDIX C

Answers to Questions

Chapter 1

1. A drawing, using symbols to represent the various parts, which shows the electrical connections of all components in a circuit. In addition, the value of components, color of leads, tube pin connections, voltage and resistance measurements, and many other items are usually included.
2. By a code letter and number.
3. It shows the various stages in the unit, and how they fit together.
4. The physical location of the components.
5. It shows each part as it actually looks in the chassis and is less expensive to produce.
6. They are the quickest, easiest, and most meaningful method of conveying the electrical connections within a circuit.
7. By an "exploded" view, which shows all the parts in their relative position, yet spreads them out so you can see each individual part.

8. The physical location of tubes and major components on top of the chassis. Certain items below the chassis may also be indicated by dashed lines.
9. Dial-cord strings, exploded views of record changers and tape recorders, motor-driven systems, and mechanical actions in organs or similar units.
10. The schematic.

Chapter 2

1. Ohm.
2. (A) To limit current (flow of electrons) in a circuit.
   (B) To provide a voltage drop.
3. An opposition to the flow of electrons through a circuit. The electrical equivalent of friction.
4. Omega (Ω).
5. A variable resistor.
6. R.
7. 27,000 ohms.
8. One whose reactance decreases when its temperature is increased.
9. ⎯⋀⋀⋀⎯

10.

Chapter 3

1. To store electrons.
2. No, they only appear to.
3. The farad.
4. The dielectric.
5. No.
6. Filter capacitors in power supplies.
7. One millionth.
8. The rotor.
9. C.
10. (A) Polarized electrolytic capacitor. (B) Trimmer capacitor. (C) Nonpolarized electrolytic.

Chapter 4

1. Inductance.
2. Henry.
3. None, except for the slight amount of resistance it offers to the flow.
4. The magnetic lines of force set up by the primary cut the secondary winding.
5. Two or three solid lines (═══ or ══).
6. Choke.
7. The primary.
8. A powdered-iron core.
9. T and L.
10.

Chapter 5

1. To control the flow of electrons.
2. To supply or emit electrons.
3. V
4. A gas tube.
5. The television picture tube.
6. The plate.
7. Through pins in the tube base.
8.

9.

10.

Chapter 6

1. Germanium, silicon, selenium.
2. It is not necessary.
3. Npn and pnp.
4. Base, collector, and emitter.
5. Source, gate, and drain.
6. ─▶│─
7. ─▶│─
8.
9.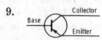
10. Voltage regulation.

Chapter 7

1. To open and close a circuit.
2. Single-pole, single-throw.
3. Single-pole, double-throw.
4. To connect one point to either of two other points.
5. An electrically operated switch.
6. The two points are mechanically (but not electrically) connected.
7. To form an electromagnet.
8. S, SW, M, E
9.
10.

Chapter 8

1. To convert an electrical signal into sound waves.
2. A fuse.
3. Incandescent and neon.
4. A cell is the basic unit; a battery is a group of cells.
5. Carbon, dynamic (or moving coil), capacitor, ceramic, and crystal.
6.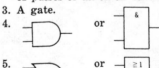
7.
8.
9.
10. A circuit breaker.

Chapter 9

1. It simplifies the layout of the schematic by eliminating many lines.
2. Plug section.
3. Not always, but they can be.
4. A bus line.
5. The same as for any other leads.
6. Occupy less space; less expensive in initial cost; and less expensive to assemble on chassis.
7. A shielded component.
8. That they are parts of a multiple unit.
9.
10.

Chapter 10

1. To convert ac to dc.
2. One to which power must be supplied.
3. No electrons will flow.

4. Npn and pnp.
5. The cathode follower.
6. From emitter to collector.
7. The cathode.
8. Common emitter, common base, and common collector.
9. Grounded cathode, grounded grid, and cathode follower.
10. The negative terminal.

Chapter 11

1. At the upper left-hand corner.
2. Rf amplifier, oscillator, mixer.
3. Color of leads.
4. To automatically compensate for changes in signal strength.
5. In frequency only.
6. Break it down into individual stages.
7. Audio signal.
8. If one burns out, all tubes will go out.
9. Speaker.
10. To remove high-frequency signals present in the circuit.

Chapter 12

1. One which deals with directly measurable variable quantities.
2. One which deals with a series of pulses or an on-off condition.
3. A gate.
4. 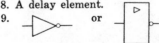 or
5. or
6. OR.
7. Exclusive OR gate.
8. A delay element.
9. or
10. 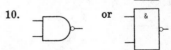 or

Index

Iron—cont
  -core
    coils, powdered, 54
    transformers, 59-60
  dust, 54

J

Junction
  field-effect transistor, 88
  pn, 80-82

K

Key, locating, 65
Knife switch, 100

L

Laminations, 55
Lamps, 120-121
  fluorescent, 120
  incandescent, 120
  neon, 121
Layout diagrams, chassis, 14
Letter codes
  diodes, 84
  rectifiers, 83
Light-dependent resistor, 36
Lines, dashed, 19
Locating key, 65
Logic symbols, 177

M

Machines, rotating, 130-131
Magnet, permanent, 126
Magnetic field, 51
Material, insulating, 39
Mechanical diagrams, 17, 19
Mercury, 121
Megohm, 26
Metal
  envelope, 64
  oxide semiconductor field-effect
    transistor, 88
Metalized resistor, 27
Meters, 132
Methods of denoting connections,
  other, 137-138
Mica, 42
Microfarad, 40
Microhenry, 52
Microphones, 123-125
Millihenry, 52
Mixing, 70
Modulating, 123
Modules, 148
Monopole antenna, 113
Motors, 130-131
Moving-coil microphone, 123

Multifunction tubes, 71-72
Multisection capacitor, 47

N

NAND gate, 174-175
Negative temperature coefficient, 36
Negator, 176
Neon lamps, 121
Nickel-cadmium, 121
Nonpolarized, 47
NOR gate, 175
Nucleus, 19

O

Octal-base tube, 65
Ohms, 26
Omega, 26
OR gate, 174
  exclusive, 175-176
Oscillators, delay lines, and ampli-
  fiers, 176-177
Oxide, film, 43

P

Packaged electronic circuits, 145-
  148
Paper, wax impregnated, 40
Parametric diode, 94
Path, signal, 159, 161-163
Pentagrid tubes, 70
Pentode tubes, 68-69
Permanent magnet, 126
Permeability, 54
  tuning, 54
Phenolic forms, 52
Phono pickups, 127-128
Photodiodes, 95
Photoemissive-type diode, 95
Photographs and pictorial dia-
  grams, 15-17
Photomultiplier, 73
Phototubes, 72-73
Pickup(s)
  phono, 127-128
  sonar, 126
Picofarad, 40
Pictorial diagrams and photo-
  graphs, 15-17
Piezoelectric effect, 122
Pinch-off, 88
Placement chart, transistor, 14
Plastic films, 42
Plate(s), 39-40, 63
  beam forming, 70
  Pn junction, 80-82
Polarity, 47
Polycarbonate, 42
Polyester, 42